Laughter Doesn't Hurt

Feel Better, Live Longer and Have
More Fun With Your Own
Built-In Smile

Includes a two month's supply of
Comedy Vitamins

by

Dale Irvin

Laughter Doesn't Hurt
Feel Better, Live Longer and Have More Fun With Your Own Built-In Smile

Copyright © MCMXCVII ~ Dale Irvin

Printed in the United States of America

ISBN 0-9657420-0-8
Library of Congress No. 97-071312

Cover & Layout Design:
Ad Graphics, Tulsa, Oklahoma

Photo by Robert Kim

Published by:

Kleenan Press

Dedication

This book is dedicated to the
memory of my parents.

The Personalized Dedication Page

When you buy this book, and want to customize it for yourself, simply tear out this page. Then, add your name on the line of the following page. Your friends will think this entire masterpiece was dedicated to you.

Dedication

This book is dedicated to my best friend

and source of inspiration

Lou-Anne & Terry

I could not have done it without him/her.

Them

Forward

I have never understood what the FORWARD of a book is supposed to do. Is it supposed to encourage you to read the book by subliminally telling you to "Go forward in this book"? Or is it designed to show you which end of the book is the beginning? If this is true, shouldn't there be a chapter at the end of the book entitled, BACKWARD?

Oops, wait a minute, I think the heading of this page has been mispelled. What it should really say is...

Forword

This is completely different. Everybody knows what a FORWORD is. It is that part of the book that comes before the rest of the book. Well, there you have it.

This is the end of the FORWORD. Please continue on to THE REST OF THE BOOK.

Contents

Introduction

This is a book about laughter. In it you will read about the healing benefits of laughter and how a daily dose of laughter can help you live longer, live happier, and have more fun.

The secret is in the picture shown on the cover of this book, the human skull. Take a good look at it and it appears as if the human skull is smiling; and a smile is the precurser to a laugh. This tells me that when God invented man, he intended for us to laugh because he built it into the hard drive. All we have to do is to bring it to the surface and let it out.

As you read this book, think about what is happening inside your own head right now. Underneath all of that skin, your skull is already smiling. So don't fight it, let it be free. Bring that smile to the surface and laughter will follow.

The last 197 pages of this book allow you to put into practice the tips you learned in the first 36 pages. The "Comedy Vitamins" as I call them are a collection of funny stories designed to make you laugh. If you start each day with one funny story, you will have a two-month supply. If one of the months is February, you will have even more than a two-month supply.

For reading ease, you may wish to keep this book in the bathroom since that is where we do the majority of our reading. Then each morning as you are...sitting down, you can take a comedy vitamin and look forward to the rest of the day.

Just in case you don't read this introduction, I have explained the concepts of the skull and the Comedy Vitamins elsewhere in the book. But if you did read the introduction all the way down to here...good for you.

Now, let's take a look at why "Laughter Doesn't Hurt."

If It Doesn't Taste Bad, Make You Dizzy, Or Hurt Like Hell, It Must Not Be Medicine

Sure, it's a long chapter title, but it's true isn't it? We were all brought up under the notion that medicine has to taste bad, side effects are natural, and doctors can only cure you with needles, scalpels, and rubber glove clad fingers. Well to this I say "bull squat!" And trust me, I very rarely say "bull squat", opting for the more familiar colloquial term.

For starters, let me point out that I am not a doctor. I don't even play one on TV. Once or twice I have played one on a date but that is a story for another book. The point is that I have no educational background in the field of medicine. I don't know the difference between an embolism and an arboretum, but I learned early in life that laughing makes you feel better inside than just about anything else in the world.

A few years ago a man by the name of Norman Cousins had this same idea. He wrote a book that changed my life entitled "Anatomy Of An Illness" wherein he documented how his ability to laugh helped to heal him from a disease called ankylosing spondilitis. Actually, just saying ankylosing spondilitis out loud several times will cause one to laugh, but that aside, he found laughter had such a positive effect on the chemistry of the human body that it actually allowed him to recover from a disease to which his doctors said there was no cure.

If you have never had the pleasure of reading Cousins' book, I suggest you do so right after you finish this one. With that in mind, allow me to proceed with my ideas for a healthy life.

Why Laugh?

Why not?! Laughing doesn't cost anything, it won't make you fat, it doesn't cause cancer, it won't make you pregnant, it will not stain your teeth, it does not cause your hair to fall out, and it will not give you acne.

On the other hand, it WILL make you feel good, it will give you a heightened feeling of pleasantness, it exercises your face, your chest, and your abdomen, it helps relieve headache pain, it relieves stress, it lowers your blood pressure, and it helps you digest Italian food. In other words, there is NOTHING WRONG WITH LAUGHTER. Even the EPA, the DEA, and the FDA could find nothing harmful about laughing. And the best part is that LAUGHTER IS FREE! [1]

What we have here is something that feels good to do, is good for you, and doesn't cost anything. It's kind of like what sex was like in the Garden of Eden before Eve screwed up and ate the apple. In fact, I'll bet that's why God gave us laughter, because he knew that sex would eventually become dangerous and/or costly.

---

[1] Yes, I know that this book cost $12.95 and it's sole purpose is to make you laugh so therefore, laughter costs $12.95, but for the sake of the concept just run with me, O.K.?

I am convinced that laughter is, in fact, a divine gift. If you doubt me just take a look at the picture on the cover of this book. It is a skull and it is smiling. Each of our skulls has a pre-installed smile, and since a smile is the precursor to a laugh, I am convinced that when God created man that he intended for us to laugh because HE BUILT IT IN TO THE HARD DRIVE!

Besides being standard equipment on every human, laughter is good for you. Research has proven that when you laugh, you exercise 15 muscles in your face as well as a number of equally important muscles in your chest and your abdomen. In fact, if you wind up experiencing convulsive laughter where you are literally flopping around on the floor like a salmon out of water, then even your arms and your legs get a workout. In addition, laughter exercises the lungs and the heart by making you breathe more and making your blood pump faster. This is good. Breathing and blood are two things that are very important to life. And if laughter makes either one of them work better, I say, "Good for it."

But here is the best part. When you laugh, your brain releases endorphins. Now you are probably asking yourselves, "What are those?" so I will tell you. I'm not real sure. But I know that when endorphins get out of the brain they make you feel real goofy. Sort of like when tequila gets out of the bottle. So in a way, endorphins are like tequila.....except that if you have too many endorphins you won't wake up on the front lawn with a throbbing headache and blurred vision. Endorphins are the body's own natural pain killer and they are released during periods of strenuous exercise and laughter. You tell me, which you would rather do, run twenty miles or go to a comedy club?

16

Next, laughter helps you to relieve stress. You know what stress is, it's that invisible thing that gives you a heart attack. I hope I am not becoming too technical here but I feel that this is something you should know. Stress is caused by tension, and tension is caused by....something else. But the important fact is that laughter relieves tension and therefore eliminates stress.

If you don't believe me try this simple exercise. Assume some tension by lifting something really heavy, like a small goat, over your head. Next, have someone make you laugh by either telling you jokes, tickling you, or showing you nude photos of your bowling team. When you start to laugh you will soon find that you can no longer keep the tension in your muscles necessary to hold up goat and you will drop them. So laughter takes away tension and stress, except for the stress that you will have when you realize that the goat you just dropped is now in a very grouchy mood and is running at you horns first.

Chapter

III

Is That A Joke Book In Your Pocket Or Are You Happy To See Me?

Laughter is an aphrodisiac. Don't laugh, I'm serious. You tell me who you would rather make mad passionate love with, someone who makes you laugh, or someone who can explain the European Common Market in minute detail?

Actually, recent studies point out that the number one attribute that women look for in a mate is a sense of humor. (see chapter 7) The same survey also pointed out that the number one thing that men look for in a mate are big hooters.

Next time you attend a cocktail party, take a good look at the person who is the center of attention. Generally it is the person who is telling jokes. Everybody loves to laugh and we like to be around people who can make us laugh. Even in business, you will find that the most successful salespeople in the market are the ones who gain your confidence by making you laugh. That must be why used car dealers wear those funny polyester clothes.

This, "make 'em laugh and close the sale" technique is not true for every business. Many of us would feel uncomfortable around a chuckling IRS agent or Shecky the Undertaker. "You're going to love this model casket, because when you open the lid, the light goes on."

Also, it is impossible to hate somebody who makes you laugh. Even your obnoxious Uncle Ed, the one who had the charisma bypass operation, seems almost human when he tells the joke about the priest and the rabbi. People who make us laugh are easier to like, and, since we all want to be liked, making others laugh is vitally important in today's world. Take world leaders for example. Ronald Reagan was one of the most loved presidents in history. Granted, he couldn't tell an economic policy from an insurance policy, but he made us laugh. He was funny and we liked him. On the other hand, Saadam Hussein has never once cracked a joke....unless he told them in Iranian, in which case we just couldn't understand them. But I think The Saad-man just doesn't have a sense of humor.

So what is the point of all this? The point is that life is short and you should laugh as much as possible. Then, share your laughter with others. This will not only brighten their day but it will get them to like you even more. How can you do this you might ask? Read the next chapter.

Chapter IV

Laughter, The Gift You Don't Have To Wrap

As pointed out in the previous chapter, it is important to share your laughter with others. It will make them feel good and it will make you look like a nice person whether you really are one or not. It is a relatively simple thing to do. Just follow along with these simple ready to use instructions.

1. Send someone a funny greeting card. We do not get very much funny mail — unless you count those Publisher's Sweepstakes things we get from Ed McMahon, so buy someone you know and/or love a Hallmark. Better yet, send them one of those off brand cards with the thinly veiled references to bodily functions or conjugal acts. Of course, reason and common sense should prevail. Christmas cards of a naked Santa or sympathy cards featuring the Three Stooges may be viewed as being in rather poor taste.

2. Tell a joke a day. Starting today, call up somebody you know and tell them a joke. If you don't know a joke, learn one[1]. If you don't know anybody you can call, put this book down now and go buy "How To Win Friends And Influence People".

---

[1] Look for joke books in the library or at the bookstore. Better yet, buy the audio tape of "Dale's Fifty Favorite Jokes." It's only $10 plus shipping and handling and available by writing to Kleenan Press. Their address is in the front of the book.

Assuming, however, that you DO know someone to call, I will start you on the way to phone jokedom with the following week's supply of jokes. Feel free to tell them in your own words but try to avoid telling the same person the same joke two or more days in a row. It will lose its impact.

MONDAY - What is the least heard phrase in the English language? Is that the banjo player's Porsche?

TUESDAY - A 90 year old woman and her 95 year old husband were watching TV one evening when the woman told her husband, "I want some ice cream from the kitchen. Write down what I want so you don't forget." Her husband responded, "I don't need to write it down, I can remember everything. Now, what do you want?". She said, "I want vanilla ice cream with chocolate sauce, chopped nuts and a cherry...WRITE IT DOWN." Again he said, "I don't need to write it down, I can remember it from here to the kitchen." Off he went to the kitchen. He returned twenty minutes later with a plate of scrambled eggs and bacon and a glass of orange juice. "You old fool", the wife yelled, "I told you to write it down." "Why?" he said, "What's wrong?" His wife yelled, "You forgot the toast!"

WEDNESDAY - A man in California was arrested for shooting and killing an eagle. When the authorities slapped the cuffs on him they asked him why on earth would he kill an eagle, the national symbol and a protected species. The man replied, "Well, I eat 'em." "You eat them?" the officer exclaimed. "What do they taste like." The man replied, "Sort of like a cross between a condor and a spotted owl."

THURSDAY - A guy walks into a bar with his dog on a leash. When the bartender tells him that they don't allow dogs in the bar the man replies, "This is my seeing eye dog". The bartender allows the man and the dog to stay.

After finishing his drink, the man leaves. On his way out he meets another man with a Chihuahua on a leash. The second man said, "Hey, how did you get your dog in the bar? They don't allow dogs in that bar." The first gentleman told him, "I told the bar tender it was my seeing eye dog."

The second man walked into the bar with his dog and sat down. The bartender immediately said, "Hey pal, no dogs in the bar." The man replied, "It's my seeing eye dog." Not easily fooled, the bartender said, "It's a Chihuahua!" To which the man replied, "They gave me a Chihuahua?!"

FRIDAY - A duck walks into a bar and says to the bartender, "You got any duck food?" The bartender looks at the duck and says, "Hey, this is a bar, we don't have duck food." The duck leaves only to return the next day and ask the bartender, "You got any duck food?" Again, the bartender tells him, "I told you yesterday, this is a bar. We don't have any duck food." On the third day, the duck returns again and asks, "You got any duck food?" The bartender is irate at this point and screams, "Look, pal, we don't have duck food in here, and furthermore, if you ever ask for it again I'm going to nail your little duck feet to the floor."

The next day, the duck comes back and looks at the bartender. "WHAT DO YOU WANT?" sceamed the bartender. "You got any nails?" said the duck. An exasperated bartender yelled, "NO, this is a bar, we don't have nails!" The duck looked at him and said, "You got any duck food?"

SATURDAY - After marrying a young filly, a ninety-year old geezer told his doctor that they were expecting a baby.

"Let me tell you a story," said the doctor. "An absent-minded fellow went hunting, but instead of a gun, he picked up an umbrella. Suddenly, a bear charged him. Pointing his umbrella at the bear, he shot and killed it on the spot."

"Impossible!" the geezer exclaimed. Somebody else must have shot that bear!"

"Exactly," replied the doctor!

SUNDAY - The local bar was so sure that its bartender was the strongest man around that they offered a standing $1000 bet. The bartender would squeeze a lemon until all the juice ran into a glass, and hand the lemon to a patron. Anyone who could squeeze one more drop of juice out would win the money. Many people had tried over time (weight-lifters, longshoremen, etc.) but nobody could do it.

One day, this scrawny little man came into the bar, wearing thick glasses and a polyester suit, and said in a tiny squeaky voice, "I'd like to try the bet." After the laughter had died down, the bartender said okay, grabbed a lemon, and squeezed away. Then he handed the wrinkled remains of the rind to the little man. But the crowd's laughter turned to total silence as the man clenched his fist around the lemon and six drops fell into the glass. As the crowd cheered, the bartender paid the $1000, and asked the little man what he did for a living. "Are you a lumberjack, a weight-lifter, or what?"

The man replied, "I work for the IRS."

3. Make somebody laugh first thing in the morning. I think that we all know how difficult it is to wake up in the morning. Because of that, many of us don't wake up in the morning at all, but prefer to wait until early afternoon. My mom was not an easy person to wake up either. In fact someone once asked her if she woke up grouchy in the morning and she replied, "No, I just let him sleep." (insert rim shot and cymbal crash here).

Seriously, you will find that your attitude for the whole day changes when the first thing you do every morning is laugh. "How do you do that?", you may ask. Well, I'll tell you. First, when you read the morning paper, do not start with the front page. There is nothing funny on the front page. By newspaper guild rules, they are obliged to print only depressing news on the front page. Also, do not begin your day with the sports section. Your team may have lost the night before and this news will also depress you. Following the same logic, do not begin your day by reading the stock quotations, the weather, or the obituaries. Instead, start with the funnies.

The reason they put comic strips in the newspaper is to make you laugh. So don't disappoint the hundreds of newspaper publishers and cartoonists in the world. Follow this simple advice and all will be right with the world. FUNNIES FIRST!

THEN, when you come across a funny comic, or perhaps an amusing Ann Lander's article, or even a headline which seems slightly out of context like this one:

___NEWS___

Haagen Dazs boss dies in a freezer full of ice cream

cut it out and leave it someplace where your spouse, or room mate, or significant other will find it. This will cause them to laugh first thing in the morning[2] and the two of you will be a happy, healthy, well adjusted couple of the nineties. Yeah, right.

[2] At least until they realize that the article they really wanted to read was on the other side of your stupid cartoon.

Chapter

V

I Think (funny)
Therefore
I Am (funny)

The best way to feel better is to feel funnier. And the best way to feel funnier is to think funnier. Therefore, if you think funnier you will feel better. Simple enough but exactly how does it work.

Well, this concept of laughter making you feel better, does not just apply to your early morning waking hours. You have to think funny all day long. Now I don't want you to walk down the street giggling like some morphined idiot, but try to look at life from a slightly different point of view. For instance, whenever I get asked the question, "Excuse me young man, do you have the correct time?" I simply look at my watch and reply, "No ma'm, I set the hands of my watch at random."

When I am in the grocery store, I like to use my sense of humor to make the time fly by more quickly. I enjoy playing little games such as looking for someone who has their shopping cart about half filled with groceries. Then, when they're not looking, I toss something else in their cart. They get quite surprised when they get up to the checkout line and discover they have five pounds of beef suet.

Also, when I am in a grocery store that features a live seafood section, I start to feel sorry for the lobsters all cooped up in that little tank. I suggest taking them out of there and letting them run around a little bit. The exercise will do them good and the look in their little crustacean eyes will say, "Thanks pal".

Always a favorite in supermarket hijinks is finding out where they keep the store microphone. Usually it is kept at the courtesy desk or conveniently located by the checkouts. Once I find the microphone, I like to make store wide announcements like, "Attention shoppers, for the next 15 minutes and 15 minutes only, all cuts of beef are only twelve cents a pound." Then, just sit back and watch the stampede to the meat counter. It's fun and it clears out the rest of the store for your shopping convenience.

Yet another wacky microphone prank is to make the following announcement: "Attention shoppers, we've hidden a one thousand dollar bill inside a box of tissues in the Kleenex aisle, you find it you keep it." This results in the closest thing I have ever seen to an indoor snow storm.

The nice thing about thinking funny is that you can do it darn near anywhere. Not just in the grocery store but in church, at the movies, in the car or while hang gliding naked over the Santa Monica Pier. The secret is to look at things the way they are, and then twist them 90 degrees. If they don't look funny, twist them again...and again, until you can see the lighter side of any situation

Case in point: In January of 1988 I was flying from New York LaGuardia to Chicago O'Hare. It was a Friday night, the plane was full, and the weather was just this side of abominable. It was cold, it was snowing, and there was about two feet of snow already on the ground. It looked like a scene out of Airport (the original Airport with Dean Martin and

Burt Lancaster, not those crappy remakes Airport 1975, Airport '77, and the ghastly The Concorde-Airport '79). Anyhow, the plane was rockin' and rollin' on the way to Chicago. The seatbelt sign was illuminated the entire trip and many of the passengers even returned their meals to the flight attendants...neatly wrapped in those little bags you find in the seat pocket in front of you. In other words, it was a rough flight. We were all looking forward to landing at O'Hare, buying some Clorets, and heading to our warm comfortable homes.

Everything was fine as we approached the runway. Everything was peachy as we touched down. Everything went to hell as we tried to stop. Apparently this plane was not equipped with anti-lock brakes and just as every passenger was pumping their feet on make-believe brake pedals, the aircraft skidded off the runway and into a huge snow drift. We were on the ground but very very stuck. Needless to say, my fellow passengers were more than a little shaken. At this point, the pilot came on the intercom and told us what we already knew, that we were stuck in a snow drift. Gosh, with a finely honed sense of the obvious like this, it was no wonder that he was the captain. He said to - I swear this is true - "Stay inside the airplane until we find out from the tower what we are going to do." STAY IN THE AIRPLANE! No way pal, I want to get out and PUSH. Come on, if we all put our backs into it we can get this baby unstuck. At this point, I wondered if the cockpit was manned by Larry, Darryl, and Darryl.

After several dozen minutes, Captain Larry came back on the intercom and informed us that we should now get out of the plane and onto busses which were coming to get us. This did not sit well with the passengers who were expecting curbside drop-off. Nonetheless[1], the doors were opened, mobile stairs were wheeled up, and we started to leave the confines of our snowbound plane.

The flight attendants stood by the door and dutifully repeated the stewardess farewell to each passenger, "Bye-bye, Bye-bye, good bye now, bye-bye, etc. ad nauseum". Each passenger, in turn uttered something about how the airline was going to hear from their respective lawyers. They were not smiling. It is at this point that I thought a little humor might be appropriate. In a voice loud enough for most passengers to hear, I asked the flight attendant, "Excuse me ma'm but do you plan on leaving this plane out here by the side of the runway all night?" She replied "Yes, why? Bye bye." I, in turn told her, "Hey, this is Chicago, in the morning this baby is going to be up on blocks and the radio's going to be missing." This impromptu humor was just what was needed. It broke the tension, it got people laughing, and it gave the stewardess an excuse to smack me with a headphone cord.

---

[1] Also spelled "Nuntheless", a 12th century religious figure of little significance. See "Peter The Great."

Take Three Belly Laughs And Call Me In The Morning

So far, I have told you about all of the fun ways you can use laughter. You can use it to impress and influence people, to garner the affections of the opposite sex (or whatever sex the kids are into garnering the attention of nowadays), to relieve stress, and to keep you from climbing atop a tall building with a high powered rifle. BUT, how, exactly does laughter keep a person from getting sick?

Well, to be brutally honest with you, it can't. But then again, to quote little old Jewish grandmothers everywhere, "Vat could it hoit?" Granted, I have never had a Jewish grandmother myself, but several of my friends with Jewish grandmothers have backed me up on this quote.

Laughter leads to healthy living in the same way that eating right and exercising do. It is common sense. If you keep your body in good spirits by feeding it the right fuel and taking it out for a walk on a regular basis, it will perform well for you. This is known as preventive medicine. Therefore, it logically follows that if you keep your mind in peak condition, it will function well for you too. But don't take it from me. In Proverbs 17:22 even God said, "A merry heart doeth good like a medicine; but a broken spirit drieth the bones." So if you don't want to go around with drieth bones, put more laughter into your life.

A lot of research has been done on this subject by a lot of people who have a lot better grade point average than I ever had, so I have to believe them. Among other things, these researchers found the following:

☺ Laughter helped to increase a person's threshold of pain.

☺ Laughter helped individuals fight off the anger, depression, fatigue, and anxiety related to cancer and its treatment.

☺ Laughter helps you to live longer. (Hey, even if it doesn't actually help you live longer, at least it makes the time you spend here a lot more fun.)

☺ Laughter can help promote the production of killer cells, found in the body to fight certain diseases and some cancers.

In some cases, the research was done first hand. Jim Brady was President Ronald Reagan's press secretary. In the 1981 assassination attempt on the president, Jim Brady was hit by a bullet intended for the president and suffered severe brain damage. In fact three networks reported that he was DEAD. However, to paraphrase Mark Twain, reports of his death were greatly exaggerated. He spent nine months in the hospital and returned home in a wheel chair. He was given little chance for recovery. But HE DID RECOVER. He's not at 100% but then I think that if you ask him, he'd tell you that he isn't done recovering yet.

Among the things that Brady credits with his remarkable recovery is the love of his family and his sense of humor. To quote him, "If I didn't have a sense of humor, they would have carted me off a long time ago."

Laughter is not the magic cure-all for everything that ails you. I wish it were because then I could charge as much as a doctor. But it isn't. On the other hand, I don't think there is a medicine or medical technique in existence that is a certain cure-all for every sickness. Laughter is definitely part of an ongoing therapy; a therapy which will not only help to keep you healthier but will help to ease the pain when you are sick.

VII

Drop And Give Me Twenty Punchlines

If you're like me, you could probably go for a beer right about now. Also, if you're like me, you're not to crazy about exercising. In fact, exercise ranks right up there with paper cuts, root canal work and blood letting in your list of favorite activities. Well, my friends, fear no more because I have discovered a no-pain alternative for the dreaded exertion of physical training. Are you ready for this? It's LAUGHTER.

I'm serious. Laughter is the new alternative to spending hours in the gym wearing one of those thick leather belts so that when you lift weights your kidneys don't shoot out of your body. It also beats spending hours running around the track until your eyes bug out and you get short of breath and feeling like you are going to die so you take a shower and a sauna with a bunch of naked guys who make you feel uncomfortable because you are not really into seeing other guys naked if you know what I mean. In other words, laughter beats exercise.

What do you get when you exercise, other than hot, sweaty, and tired? OK, you get a better looking body that runs like a finely tuned German automobile. Big deal. Muscles are not all they're cracked up to be. Sure, a good body might help you attract a good looking member of the opposite sex but guess what???? SO DOES LAUGHTER.

When was the last time that you saw a beautiful woman walking down the street with a guy who looked like the elephant man's ugly cousin? It happens all of the time and more times than not it is not even a hostage situation. So what gives? Well, I'll tell you. The woman is obviously not attracted to the man's lumpy body, pot belly, triple chins, or misshapen nose. She is attracted to him because he makes her laugh.

My suggestion is that you quit going to the health club and spend your time sitting on the couch reading joke books. Memorize as many jokes as you can until you feel confident with your new found comedy shape. Then, go out into society and show up all of those muscle heads by picking up their women with a punchline, a few riddles, and a well timed knock knock joke. Trust me, women will be fawning all over you. Some in fact will go beyond fawning and will proceed to full fledged deerdom where they will tie you onto their car bumpers and take you home.

The Comedy Vitamins

This, no doubt, is the reason you bought this book. When you can buy a two month supply of ANYTHING for the small price you paid for this publication you are getting one heck of a deal. BUT I SHOULD WARN YOU, comedy vitamins are not like regular vitamins. There are several important differences.

☺ Comedy Vitamins are meant to be READ. DO NOT TAKE THEM INTERNALLY. Now before you say "Hey, Dale, what do we look like, idiots?" let me just say that I had to include this disclaimer for legal reasons. All I need is a lawsuit from some bonehead who ripped out a page of vitamins, wadded it up, swallowed it, and caused himself severe digestive distress. So I am not talking to you, the intelligent reader, I am talking to the doofus looking to sue me for money I don't have.

☺ It is recommended that Comedy Vitamins, like real vitamins, be taken once a day. BUT, if you feel you need an extra dose of comedy to jolt your funny bone, feel free to read two, three, or more vitamins at one sitting. You will cause no bodily injury since it is impossible to overdose on laughter.

☺ Comedy Vitamins are not required by law to have a child-proof cap. If, for any reason, you do not want your children reading these vitamins, it is your responsibility to keep them in a safe place. BUT, there is nothing in the Comedy Vitamins that I would not let children read unless you are afraid of the questions they may ask you afterward.

☺ KEEP DRY. Comedy Vitamins, like the regular kind, work best if they are kept nice and dry. You will find that the pages turn easier when they are dry, and the print will not become blurry. If, however, you get them wet by reading them in the swimming pool or dropping them in the toilet, you can easily dry them out with a hair dryer.....but don't expect the book to look quite as nice as it does now.

☺ Start your dosage today. If you read one Comedy Vitamin per day you should run out of them just in time to purchase my next book. Gosh, isn't that a great marketing ploy?

Who Was The 17th King Of Sweden?

I love trivia. I play Trivial Pursuit. I watch Jeopardy. I can even name all of the original cast members of Petticoat Junction, but no matter how much I learn, there seems to be so much more to discover. To help you unlock the fun and excitement of trivia, I have developed the following trivia test. It will challenge you and maybe even frustrate you, but it will also make you smarter than you were just a few seconds ago.

Dale's Trivia For Everyone

Easy

1. What color is an orange?

2. What has four legs, is furry, and barks?

3. What do you call an uncircumcised Jewish baby?

Medium

4. What is the most popular pastime among lemmings?

5. If two wrongs don't make a right, what does make a right?

6. What happened when the Pope went to Mount Olive?

Difficult

7. Howdy Doody's brother was named Double Doody (true). What was Howdy's dog's name?

8. What do you do with an elephant with three balls?

9. How does Don King get his hair to do that?

10. What do you get when you cross a hooker with Robert Fulton?

Answers

1. I don't believe you even thought about this one.

2. A dog. That's why this is the easy category.

3. A girl.

4. Follow The Leader.

5. Three lefts make a right.

6. Popeye darn near killed him.

7. Flubadub. He decided on this name because Doggie Doody sounded like something that you might step in.

8. Walk him and pitch to the giraffe.

9. I don't know but it is protected by the National Park Service as a wildlife refuge.

10. A tramp steamer

2

Take Me Out To The Ball Game

The crack of the bat; the roar of the crowd; the taste of a hot dog...all filled with rodent hairs and bug bits; the smell of the men's washroom; the sight of your new car resting on blocks with its radio, tires and engine missing because you were too cheap to pay ten bucks for a parking lot; ah, you just can't beat it - the sensations that surround the arrival of baseball season.

When the Boys of Summer get ready to play they also get ready to snort cocaine, chase women, and charge $6 for their autograph. Is it any wonder that baseball is called America's Favorite Pastime?

If you're like me, you really love baseball and try to attend as many games as possible, but you aren't sure of the proper etiquette to be displayed at the ball park. Well, stop your worrying. As a public service I am very proud to present....

Dale's Guide To Ball Park Behavior

Attire: A baseball game is an informal affair. In fact, it is so informal that if you have the bad taste to show up wearing a coat and tie, it is within all reasonable boundaries for other spectators to spill beer and/or mustard on you. I would suggest wearing attire emblazoned with the name of the home team. This can include T-shirts, shorts, socks, or tattoos. Women are urged to wear halter tops or something equally skimpy so that guys have something to ogle during the boring innings. Men are requested not to remove their shirts no matter how hot it is or how large their stomach is. Women, however, can take off anything they like.

Food: The nice thing about going to baseball games is that you can eat things which you would normally reserve for use in science experiments. Tasty items primordial hot dogs, warm, syrupy Cokes, and of course, BEER. Actually, beer is the only thing that you should really consume at a ball park. It's natural, it's refreshing, and it's a mild diuretic.

Proprieties: Always stand during the national anthem. Sing along only if you KNOW ALL OF THE WORDS. Take off your cap and hold it over your heart. Start cheering like an idiot when the singer gets to the "O're the land of the free" part and keep right on yelling through the end of the song, at which time you may replace your cap, high five the person sitting next to you, and continue drinking your 17th beer.

If, at any time, the occupants of the ball park decide to do the "wave", DO NOT JOIN THEM. In fact, when the "wave" comes around to you, stand up and slug the person sitting next to you as hard as you can while screaming "Death to the wave". This will probably get you tossed out of the park, but hey, you made a statement and, more than likely, will wind up on the 6 o'clock news.

In the event that a foul ball flies in your direction, all laws regarding decency and common sense are negated. In other words, do whatever you have to do to get your paws on that ball. I'm not kidding, when it comes to catching a foul ball, I would stiff arm Mother Theresa if I thought she was in my way.

Post Game Procedure: Since most baseball games are very crowded, there is usually a crowd control problem after the game. Generally there are two accepted ways of handling this situation. You can either A) fight the crowd at the conclusion of the game until you get to your car at which point you will be stuck in traffic for three hours or B) leave in the fifth inning. Option B was invented by L.A. Dodger fans and is used with such regularity that the entire park empties out after the fifth inning and they all sit in a traffic jam for three hours. I offer one more solution to beat the flock. Simply wait until the game is over and remain in your seat until EVERYBODY has gone home. Now, you have the ball park to yourself. You can run around the bases if you like. You can take batting practice. You can even spit on home plate just like the stars. Then, when you have all the fun you care to have, hop the fence and head on home in uncrowded tranquillity.

3

Spring Ahead, Fall Down

My good friend and resident alter ego, Eddie Lubitsch works for my monthly publication, Funny Business, where he is in charge of writing the monthly editorial under his byline, "The Last Angry Man". I have asked Eddie to submit a few articles for this book and he has graciously accepted with the caveat that I do not attempt to change his writing style. With that in mind, here is the first of several entries by Eddie Lubitsch, The Last Angry Man.

Spring is here. Great big hairy deal! I really don't like Spring. I never have and I probably never will. Why, you may ask? Well, Mr. or Mrs. Curiosity, I shall tell you.

First of all, I hate Spring because it comes too early in the year. The first day of Spring is officially March 20th and I don't know about you but where I live it is still colder than a walrus' willy on March 20th. If Spring is supposed to be the harbinger of warm weather, move it back to a month where it is warm...like May. March is just too early to start Spring.

Eventually Spring does warm up - and then what happens? The snow in the back yard melts and suddenly all of the dog doo that has laid dormant all winter long is dangerous again. When the snow disappears, my back yard looks like a minefield in Bosnia, and let me tell you, there is nothing more disgusting than a field of formerly frozen Fido feces to really make you hate Spring.

Next on my list of Springtime annoyances is that

Spring means Easter and Easter means good old Eddie has to shell out big bucks for new clothes for the family. Every Easter I have to buy all new duds for Estelle and the kids and this really gets under my skin. Why can't the damn kids wear the same clothes they did last year? I do and I am quite the snappy dresser, even if I do say so myself. I will just dust off the old bell bottoms and my favorite Nehru jacket and I will be ready for the Easter Parade....which is something else that bugs me.

You always hear about this Easter Parade but I have yet to find one. They don't put it on TV like the Rose Bowl Parade or Macy's Thanksgiving Day Parade. They don't even have any floats for crying out loud. Who is in charge of this bogus parade? I want some answers. I want some heads to roll. I want some marching bands and pompom girls in short skirts.

By far and away, the most prominent peeve I have with the approach of the vernal equinox is the fact that everything starts to grow again. The flowers grow, the grass grows, and the damn weeds grow. This means Eddie has to spend every spare minute pushing the old Lawn Boy around the yard while trying not to step in the strategically placed dog biscuits. And it's fancy footwork like this that really tweaks my tulips and makes me, The Last Angry Man.

That's all from me....for now.

4

Hey,
I'm Outta Paper In Here

As Americans, we tend to read quite a bit. In fact, reading is one of the things which makes us literate. Granted, we don't always read things which will make us smarter, improve our lives, or aid in the general welfare. Our reading may consist of nothing more than perusing the directions on a bag of microwave popcorn, but at least we are reading.

We also read in many different places. Sometimes we read in the library. Sometimes we read on an airplane. And sometimes we even read in school. But the number one site for American's reading is the bathroom. "Why is this?" you might ask. Well, we like to read in our bathrooms because Americans have the best darned bathrooms on the face of the planet. Our bathrooms are well lighted and adequately ventilated places of repose. The average US bathroom is the epitome of tranquillity. If you don't believe me, go to the bathroom in Europe some time.

I encourage reading in the bathroom. In fact, I even considered publishing this book on a big roll of toilet paper so that you could read it in the bathroom and then provide instant editorial feedback. Most folks, however, prefer to read a different kind of paper in the bathroom. They like to start their day straddling the commode with a copy of their daily newspaper.

Some people like to enter the bathroom with the comic section of the newspaper while others prefer the sports section. I know of one fellow who likes to take the business section so that he can watch his investments go down the toilet the same time he does. Personally, I look forward to entering the washroom with the entire Sunday Chicago Tribune. It's a great way to spend several hours away from the household hub-bub. After a while, however, other family members may come looking for you. They will bang on the door inquiring, "Whatcha do, fall in?". Sometimes even my dog becomes agitated by my time spent in the bathroom and gives me one of those looks that means, "You know, you're sitting on my water dish in there!"

Another choice for your latrine literature is The Congressional Record. This daily journal is available FREE to all Americans. All you have to do is write to the U.S. Department of Wasting Ink And Paper to request a subscription. Then, settle back on the hopper and experience the theory of Garbage In - Garbage Out.

The problem with bathroom reading is that many of us discover too late that we have entered the water closet without adequate reading material...sort of like being up the creek without a periodical. When this happens we can really be in dire straits. We are reduced to reading things like hair spray cans, toothpaste tubes, and the ever popular shampoo bottles. Realizing this, I think that it is the duty of every shampoo manufacturer to print more meaningful labels on their bottles. Have you ever read a shampoo bottle? Of course you have. It's boring. "Directions: Wet hair. Lather. Rinse. Repeat." B-O-R-I-N-G. How many times can a person read that same paragraph?

I think it's time for the shampoo manufacturing folks to show a little creativity. How about printing short stories on the shampoo bottles? Perhaps they could consider a condensed novel. Maybe they could even print fortunes like you find in Chinese cookies, "You find yourself doing important business" or even a more philosophical approach, "The moons shines brightly over swirling blue waters."

Wherever you decide to read, make sure that you find the time to do it because if it weren't for reading, you'd probably be using this book as kindling.

5

What's In A Name?

We all have them, we all use them, and other people never remember them. What are they? Why, our names of course. We all have names, in fact, most of us have three, a first name with which we refer to ourselves, a middle name which we hate because it used to belong to a dead family member, and a last name that we are stuck with for our whole lives unless we decide to change it.

Some of us only need one name like Moses, Elvis, Cher, or Flipper. Some of us have many names like George Herbert Walker Bush and John Jacob Jingleheimer Smith. Still others of us may have names that we don't even use because we prefer to opt for initials like ET or his brother Mr. T. Then there's the "artist" formerly known as Prince who has changed his name to something like Ω≈†®§¥.

Many of us do not like our names, wishing that we had been named something cooler. I know that I often wished that I had been named "Doctor" so that I could get good seats in a restaurant. I don't think people should change their names without reason, but one person in history would have been completely justified in changing her name.

In 1882, James Hogg thought he could gain political attention by naming his pretty baby daughter the ugly name of Ima - that's right, Ima Hogg. This poor kid had to go through her entire life telling people her name was Ima Hogg which immediately raises a question in my mind. How far should a parent be allowed to go in naming their child? Do they have the right to give the kid any old name they please or should they be held accountable later in life? Could Mr. and Mrs. Howser be sued by their son Doogie? Could the Head family face legal reprisal by naming their son Dick? And is there anything the Little Rascals could have done to their parents to pay them back for names like Spanky, Buckwheat, Porky, and Stymie? I think it is time to establish a few laws to prevent the mindless naming of our children. Here are my suggestions:

1) All cute names are to be banished from society. No longer would babies be given names like Muffin, Sugar, or Moonbeam.

2) No one should be allowed to give a child a first name that matches up with his or her last name to make something funny like Jean Poole, Jim Shoo, Ben Dover, or Hugh Jass.

3) All kids should be allowed to change their names on their 10th birthday. There is nothing worse than a kid who aspires to become a professional football player and is saddled with a name like Chauncy or Percival.

4) No creative spellings should ever be allowed, thereby prohibiting the uses of Kandee, Cyndy, or Phred.

5) Finally, no one should be allowed to put their name on a vanity license plate, thus eliminating auto tags like BOBS TOY or SUE ME. From here on in, if you want plates to match your name, you will have to change your name to match your plates. From now on you can just call me QL5739T.

6

It's A Dog Eat Dog World And I'm Wearing Milkbone Underwear

Let me begin by saying that I am a dog lover, although there are no convictions to prove it. What I mean is that I am a canine aficionado. I like dogs. I like dogs better than I like people, and the reason is very simple. Dogs will never ask you to lend them money; they will never ask you for a ride to the airport; and they will never try to sell you Amway. To be fair, however, most humans will not try to hump your leg, pee on your oriental rug, or bring a dead squirrel to your back porch.

As I write this piece, I am being watched by my new dog. I have a new dog because my old dog, after 15 years of faithful service, went to doggie heaven to visit Lassie, Rin Tin Tin, and Old Yeller. When she died, I felt the need to get another dog for companionship and a loving relationship. What I got was the dog from Hell.

I don't know why I selected my new dog from the variety of breeds available at the local animal shelter. It could have been because he bore a striking physical resemblance to my old dog. It could have been human/canine chemistry. Or it could have been because I heard him speak to me. I distinctly heard him say, "Hey pal, are you looking for a good dog? I'd be perfect for you. Come on, Sport, what do you say? Give it a shot, take me home."

I swear I heard those words coming from my dog's muzzle, but what I didn't realize at the time was that the German Shepherd in the next cage was an accomplished ventriloquist.

I brought the dog home and named him Cody because I thought he looked a lot like Kathie Lee Gifford's kid. He (my dog, not Kathie Lee's kid) is what animal people call a mixed breed. The rest of us would call him a mutt. This canine of questionable parentage was originally suspected of being part Beagle, part Husky, and part Shepherd. After thorough inspection I found him to be part Wolf, part Velociraptor, and part Satan.

All dogs seem to establish a daily schedule of activities. Here's Cody's:

6:00 AM   Bark loudly. Awaken everyone within a two mile radius.

6:15 AM   Stop barking long enough to throw up.

                 7:00 AM Eat some socks he found on the floor and a Mr. Turkey hot dog he found in the refrigerator behind the dill pickles and the cheese log.

8:00 AM   Bark until he gets fed.

8:01 AM   Eat. Then, run around in circles while growling something that sounds like "Red Rum, Red Rum."

8:15 AM   Pee in my slippers.

9:00 AM   Lick his privates and go to sleep.

11:00 AM   Wake up and bark very excitedly as the mailman approaches within 5 miles of my house.

NOON   Break something and go to sleep.

4:00 PM   Pee in the yard to create another brown patch in the mosaic that used to be a lawn. His motto is, "Where Cody goes, nothin' grows."

5:15 PM   Dig holes, eat rocks, and scare the hell out of the elderly neighbor lady who tries to make it out to her garbage can and back before he kills her.

7:00 PM   Sleep

10:15 PM   Bark loudly during the 10 O'clock News so that I miss the sports because I have to take him for a walk again.

MIDNIGHT Sleep. Bark. Pee in the kitchen. Sleep.

Do not tell me to take this dog for training. He has had training. In fact, he was suspended from obedience school for rear ending a Poodle. He has also been to a personal trainer and has seen countless doggie motivational videos. He has even been to a canine psychologist who wouldn't let him up on the couch. I've tried everything with this animal short of exorcism. I guess I'm stuck with him but I'll tell you one thing, the next time he pees in my slippers, I'm going to chew on his rawhide bone. That ought to teach him!

Hooked On Fonix

If you can read this, give thanks that you are literate. Imagine what the world would be like if no one knew how to read. Playboy Magazine would consist of nothing but pictures and television performers would use blank cue cards. No doubt about it, reading is FUNdamental.

The big problem in America today is that thousands of people still can't read. I saw a man down on his luck the other day who was holding up a sign near the expressway that read, "Will Work For Fud". I stopped to tell him that he had misspelled the word FOOD but he told me that he was only willing to work for the fictional cartoon character, Elmer Fudd. So I told him he misspelled that too.

We've got to get a better grasp of our language so that future generations will not only be able to read, but they will be able to use our native tongue properly. We need to start by ridding the language of homonyms, those pesky words that sound the same but have different meanings. They are too dang confusing to the majority of people.

Take, for example, the word SAX. This word can be spelled different ways that all sound alike and have different meanings. For instance, "Bill Clinton plays the SAX." Or, "Put them groceries in some SAX." Or, "Two plus fo be SAX." Or, "Hey baby, let's you and me get nekkid and have SAX."

See what I mean? It's confusing. Here's another example. Look at the word HOE. It can have several different meanings depending upon how the word is used. "The garden is full of weeds, I guess I'll need a HOE." Or, "If you don't pay full price you buy HOEsale." Or, "We have to bury this dead squirrel, better dig a HOE." Or, the ever popular, "Man, don't you be callin' my woman a HOE."

Without a doubt, the most confusing and mis-used of the homonyms is the word BISECTS. It can be used in the mathematical term, "Line A BISECTS line B at the vortex." It can also be used as a com-plaint such as, "Man, if my wife don't give me some lovin' I'm gonna have to go out and BISECTS." It can even be used to describe a new breed of mosquito, "These bugs will mate with either males or females, that makes them BISECTS."

Wise up America. Let's straighten out our lan-guage now before we all wind up RUSHIN' around trying to learn to speak RUSHIN'.

Rock And Roll Makes Me Hungry

An extremely rare occurrence happened to me recently. As a full moon glowed outside my window, I waxed nostalgic for the music of my youth. In an attempt to recapture that music, I spent three hours in front of the television watching MTV.

In case you are terminally un-hip, MTV, and its more sedate sibling, VH-1, are the music television stations of Generation X. They play all of the current hits as well as a limited number of videos that were made from footage of the "older" bands that you and I would remember. I spent the better part of my day relaxing in the old Lazy Boy while sipping on a tasty malt beverage.

Note: When I use the term "malt beverage" I am referring to BEER, and not that hideous beverage substance named Zima which advertises itself as a malt beverage but is really a combination of grain alcohol and seltzer water. To coin a phrase from their own ad campaign, "Zima, It Zucks."

I was having quite a good time until I started paying attention to the names of some of the musical groups whose images danced before me. I noticed names like Snoop Doggie Dogg, 10,000 Maniacs, Crash Test Dummies, Pearl Jam, and Alice In Chains. What the heck is going on here? Where are these kids getting the names of their bands?

Pardon me for sounding old but WHEN I WAS A KID bands had real names that meant something. If our bands had names with a number in them, the number referred to the total count of band members, such as The Kingston Trio, The Four Tops or The Dave Clark Five. Don't tell me there are actually 10,000 Maniacs in that band. They could never all fit on stage. And we had bands with names like Three Dog Night whose name referenced the total number of dogs you would have to sleep with on a very cold night. Snoop Doggie Dogg, on the other hand, references nothing and is not even spelled correctly[1]. How I yearn for the good old days.

As a tribute to the bands of the past, I offer the following menu of tasty band names offered for your dining and dancing pleasure at the...

Rock & Roll Diner Menu

Entrees

MEATLOAF - a basic dish made with meat and loaf and baked until it is dry and gray. It is served with a delightful sauce of RED HOT CHILE PEPPERS *(Yes, I know the RHCP are not an old band but I am taking poetic license.)*

Country Joe & THE FISH - A selection of toasted seafood served in rolling papers.

HOT TUNA - If you don't remember this selection you may as well just stop reading now.

The Flying BURRITO Brothers - This south of the border selection features a variety of musicians rolled in flour tortillas.

T-BONE Walker and T-BONE Burnett - Twin meaty treats which can be ordered as a meal or thinly sliced in a YELLOW SUBMARINE sandwich.

---

[1] Since this writing, Mr. Dogg has gone to that great fire hydrant in the sky. He was shot by a music lover.

All of the above entrees are served with BREAD, CREAM, and ICE-T.

Desserts

We offer everything to please your palate including VANILLA ICE, VANILLA FUDGE, STRAWBERRY ALARM CLOCK, and my personal favorite, MOBY GRAPE. For the more adventurous among you, the chef suggests the TANGERINE DREAM, the BANANARAMA, or the combination of fresh fruit and marijuana, otherwise known as PEACHES AND HERB.

Hike Up Your Shorts

I like lingerie. I like to look at it, I like to touch it, and I even like to spend countless hours drooling on the pages of catalogs that feature women wearing it. But I can't believe that America has a National Lingerie Week.

In this country we have National Potato Week, National Visit A Relative In Prison Week, and National Weasels As Pets Week, but I cannot see the logic of National Lingerie Week.

First of all, I find National Lingerie Week to be a very sexist celebration. I mean, it's for women only. OK, OK, there may be a few men out there who revel in the satiny softness of clingy underthings, but we are few and far between. For the most part, lingerie is for, by, and about women. Let me be the first to scream "Unfair". If women get to have a week dedicated to their undergarments, men should be able to celebrate National Boxer Shorts Day or even National Torn Underpants Day.

Women also have way too many underwear options. Unlike men whose undergarments consist of underpants (choice of boxers, briefs, or those bikini things in which no self respecting guy would be caught dead) T-shirts (crew neck, V-neck, or sleeveless) and socks (white, black, or dirty), women have numerous unmentionable options.

Women can choose from panties, G-strings, bras, teddies, camisoles (which I always thought was a kind of fancy umbrella), merry widows, garter belts, panty hose, and all of the really good stuff available from

Frederick's of Hollywood. Then, after they select the item, they must choose from a myriad of options - color or white; cotton or nylon; standard or crotchless; edible or non-edible; and if edible, which flavor. No wonder they need an entire week.

Speaking from the male perspective, I think women spend too much time on their lingerie. Sure it looks nice, especially when displayed in lunch time fashion shows at bars and restaurants catering to the horny businessman, but lingerie is really not all that important. When a man sees a woman in lingerie he is thinking only one thought, "I wonder what she looks like under that stuff."

So ladies, take note, if you really want to make an impression on men, forget National Lingerie Week and head straight for National "I Ain't Wearin' Nothin' But A Smile" Week. Trust me, I'm a guy.

10

Now Just A Dram Minute

By Eddie Lubitsch, The Last Angry Man

We are so screwed up in this country that we measure things differently than anyone else in the world. Let's start with our measurement system. While the rest of the globe uses the METRIC system of measurement, we are content to plod along with the ECLECTIC system of measurement where nothing makes any sense nor does it relate to anything else. For instance we have a foot which is 12 inches long even though no human being owns a foot which is exactly 12 inches long. And three feet make a yard, which is a pretty crappy yard by anyone's real estate standards, even for a city lot. Then we have the fortnight which is equal to 4985 bushels, the cord which equals 12.5 hectares, and the pint which equals a good buzz if it's at least 80 proof. This is all before we get into the cubit, the fathom and the angstrom. And I don't even know what AVOIRDUPOIS means but I think it has something to do with Communism.

This brings us to the mile which is different on land than it is on water. The land mile is actually SHORTER than the nautical mile. This raises an intriguing question. When you fly from New York City to London do you get credited for Frequent Flyer Miles in water miles or land miles? I think we are getting screwed big time.

Pressing on, we know that the speed in a car is measured in MILES PER HOUR, but in a boat they use the term KNOTS PER HOUR. What the hell is this. If it is called a nautical mile why do they have to come up with another term for it? And who thought of KNOTS? Why not something more positive like

SURE THINGS or YOU BETS? Then you have to wonder if a guy like Don Knotts' real name isn't Don Miles. Or if Miles Davis shouldn't have been called Knots Davis, and if Muddy Waters should just be known as Muck.

Now, let's look at how we are taking it up the old measuring cup in the volume measurement department. A DRY quart is equal to 67.201 cubic inches (3 cubic inches equals 1 cubic mouthful). But a WET quart is equal to only 57.75 cubic inches! What gives here? If I buy a quart of beer why do I get less than if I bought a quart of potato chips? This is why you always have chips left over at the end of your beer. In order to make this beer/chips ratio work out even, you would have to buy SEVEN BEERS for every SIX QUARTS of chips and BEER DOES NOT COME IN A SEVEN PACK! What if I am buying cole slaw? How is this measured? Part of it is wet and part of it is dry, so when I buy a quart of slaw, whose quart am I getting. I'm getting screwed, that's what I'm getting.

"So what are you suggesting, Eddie?" is what you are probably saying. "Do you want us to go on the metric system?" NO. This was a stupid idea when it was first introduced. Remember back in the seventies when President Jimmy "My Brother Has More Brains Than I Do" Carter tried to convert everybody to meters and liters? That worked well didn't it? To this day the only people who bought into that metric bull crap are soft drink bottlers and drug dealers. I say the answer lies in being able to come up with a measurement system which fits our needs. Throw out the pound, the quart, and the mile. In their place institute the universally recognized concepts of the scosch, the tad, and the assoff as in, "I'll have a *scosch* more mashed potatoes", or "I just dropped a *tad* of hot solder on the dog's tail", or "The Motel 6 is pretty far from here, you'll have to drive your *assoff* to make it by 6 o'clock."

Wake up America and realize that we can't go on with these archaic measurements any longer. Get on the stick IN A JIFFY, before this goes ONE TEENSY BIT further, and give us a measuring system we can use by THE BOATLOAD.

Until that happens, I shall remain The Last Angry Man.

That's all from me...for now.

11

I'm Just A Piece Of Trash And You're My Litter Bag

Hey, I think I just wrote a new country & western hit. Granted, it's no "Achy Breaky Heart" but what could compare with that? Actually this headline has nothing to do with country OR western music, but I do know what could compare to "Achy Breaky Heart"....the stuff you find in a cat's litter box compares to it nicely.

And speaking of litter boxes, did you know that April is Keep America Beautiful Month? A rational person would think that we should endeavor to keep America beautiful every month, but for some reason the U.S. Department of Designations felt that one month would be sufficient to tidy up our country.

During this month you are encouraged to perform tasks such as properly disposing of litter, picking up trash from the street, and avoid dumping toxic waste into nearby rivers and streams. It's a burden but at least we only have to do it for a month. At the end of that time America will start to collect dust again until next year when we give it the national Spring cleaning. I feel we need to concentrate more of our efforts on finding ways to keep America beautiful every month. It's what our president would call a long term beauty investment. I feel so strongly about this commitment that I have prepared a list of 19 things we can do to make America permanently more beautiful. It may be some work and some of us may be lost in the battle, but in the end we will have a much prettier country to show for it.

19 Things To Do For A More Beautiful America

1. Make ugly people wear masks.

2. Make very ugly people move to Antarctica.

3. Make having a car on blocks in your front yard punishable by death.

4. Ban the sale of lycra and spandex to fat people.

5. Wear a leisure suit - go to jail.

6. Give Don King a haircut.

7. Mandatory trimming of ear and nose hair for men over 60.

8. Print our folding money in colors and with pictures of naked babes on them.

9. Give Ted Kennedy liquor and the keys to a fast car...never mind, we tried that once before.

10. Kill that goofy Ernest guy.

11. Spruce up Indiana a little.

12. Require people with crying and/or obnoxious children to travel by Greyhound rather than air.

13. No more Brady Bunch reunion shows.

14. Establish a maximum amount of only two pierced earrings per person.

15. Do not let men buy any of their own clothing.

16. DO let men buy ALL the clothing for women.

17. Require industrial strength air fresheners for all cabs.

18. Mandatory electrolysis for swarthy women from the Balkan countries.

19. Outlaw brassieres.

Tattoo, Or Not Tattoo

I have long admired the art of tattoo. I have also admired rodeo clowns, bungee jumpers, and people who disarm bombs for a living but I don't think I would ever want to do any of these things. At least that's the way I have always thought about tattoos until recently. Lately I find myself actually THINKING about decorating my body with a tattoo. I'm just not 100% sold.

A wise man once told me that if I was ever faced with a dilemma about which I could not make a decision, that I should toss a coin and then do whatever I really wanted to in the first place. My dad was indeed a wise man but he also taught me that if you could really not decide about a predicament, that you should make a list of the pros and cons of each decision and then...do whatever you wanted to do in the first place. SO, since I am semi-seriously thinking about adorning myself with a tattoo, I have listed the pros and cons of each side of the quandary. Perhaps this will help us all decide what to do if we are faced with a similar problem.

TATTOO - THE PROS & CONS

PRO: They look cool. Tattoos tell the rest of the world that you are your own person capable of making your own decisions.

CON: If you are not good at sticking to decisions you might get stuck with the name of your ex-wife etched on your buttocks.

PRO: They attract attention.

CON: Especially the attention of the company president who is staring at the synonym for "fornicate" tattooed on your knuckles.

PRO: You never have to worry about it washing off.

CON: You also don't have to worry about it coming off even if exposed to sulfuric acid, industrial strength bleach, or a carbide tipped grinding wheel.

PRO: Numerous tattoos can virtually guarantee you employment in a carnival.

CON: They can also pretty much lock you out of a CEO position.

PRO: Some men view a tattoo on a woman as extremely sexy.

CON: Some women also view a tattoo on a woman as extremely sexy.

I think that the cons are going to win on this argument but that makes sense. Just visit any local high security prison and you will see that almost all of the cons have tattoos.

13

I Am The Man From Nantucket

If you have ever punched a cow or roped a doggie, then you should make it a point to attend the annual Cowboy Poetry Gathering in Elko, Nevada held at the end of January.

Personally, I find the concept of cowboy poets to be somewhat bizarre. Cowboys are rough and tumble kinds of guys and poets are...well let me just say that I have never seen a poet with spurs.

Now I know that some cowboys sing and play the harmonica, although not at the same time, but that is different. I grew up listening to Gene Autry, Roy Rogers, and Dale Evans singing about being back in the saddle again but I cannot for the life of me envision Billy The Kid sitting around the camp fire with a pen and paper saying, "Any of you fellers know what rhymes with LYNCH MOB?"

So, in the interest of investigative journalism, I have completed copious amounts of research into the cowboy writings of the late 1800's. To my surprise, I discovered that these cowboy poets were pretty darn good. So good, in fact, that I took the liberty of reproducing some of their more famous poems for you. Sit back, grab your branding iron, and enjoy...

FAMOUS COWBOY POEMS

While ropin' some cows on the range,
Old Buck said, "You know it's quite strange",
"The fur on that bovine,
Has started to decline,
I fear that it must be the mange."

• • • • •

• • • • •

They rode into town wearin' furs,
And tight leather pants with some spurs.
From the shine on their boots,
We thought they was fruits,
So we shot 'em. (note: not all cowboy poems rhyme.)

• • • • •

The sheriff brought in a law breaker,
And said, "Get ready to meet with your maker."
"With a rope 'round your head,
You'll hang 'till your dead,
'Cause I'm also the town's undertaker."

Always Color Inside The Lines

14

This is something that we have heard over and over again as we were growing up. In fact I still hear it when the waitress brings me that nifty place mat at Denny's on a Sunday morning. It was something that we first heard in Kindergarten.

Kindergarten is a word which has its roots in the Germanic language and can be broken down to "kinder", referring to the type of gentler nation George Bush fantasized about; and "garten" which means a place where youngsters stick clay in their ears.

Kindergarten, by the way, is the only remaining place on this planet where you will still find a cloak room. Most of America's cloak rooms have been replaced with skyscrapers or mass transit systems.

Kindergarten enjoyed a resurgence with the publishing of the best seller by Robert Fulghum entitled "Everything I Really Need To Know I Learned In Kindergarten". In this volume Mr. Fulghum expounds on many everyday topics and, unlike Salmon Rushdie (remember him?), never once makes fun of anybody who can issue a contract on your life.

The book is filled with many cute observations of life based upon things the author learned as a small child. I have to challenge his theories however, because I learned a lot after I got out of Kindergarten, not the least of which was how to open a locked car door with a coat hanger and how to unhook a woman's bra with one hand. So, as a follow up to Mr. Fulghum's book, I present my own essay on life entitled:

Everything I Really Need To Know
I Learned In College

☺ Never take a fat girl named Arlene to a fraternity party unless you want to be reminded of it for the next 30 years.

☺ In calculus class, sit next to a smart kid with poor eyesight. Chances are he will write bigger, thereby giving you a better shot at copying his answers.

☺ Never try to take your pants off without first removing your shoes.

☺ SAT scores don't mean much in the real world. Grade point averages mean even less.

☺ Spaghetti can be made in a popcorn popper, and a grilled cheese sandwich can be made with an iron.

☺ Never wash black socks with white underwear.

☺ Actually, if you wash all of your clothes together, eventually they will all match.

☺ Boone's Farm is an excellent wine with luncheon meats or Twinkies.

☺ A good stereo system is all that is really important in life.

☺ Your political views change drastically after you graduate and get a job.

☺ Never argue with a policeman with hand cuffs.

☺ Hand cuffs leave a nasty mark.

15

"...And The Home Of The Brave; Play Ball."

I think we all recognize the eight words above as the final lyrics of our national anthem, also known as The Star Spangled Banner. This national anthem has been with us for well over 200 years yet we still have a difficult time singing it. Even if we can remember all of the words, most of us cannot reach the high notes. That's just one of the reasons why I have always thought that James Brown's "Livin' In America" would be a much better anthem. It's got a nice beat, you can dance to it, and it would be a much more lively way to start a ball game. BUT, that is not what this chapter is about.

June 14th is currently Flag Day in America. Actually, it has been Flag Day for quite some time now but we don't seem to pay enough attention to it. It is not like our other holidays. No one sends Flag Day cards. We don't have Flag Day parades. Heck, we don't even make a turkey. Flag Day is a forgotten step child of a holiday but I think it is time to bring it back to national prominence.

Next Flag Day I urge you to relax in the backyard with your mother, some apple pie, and a CD of patriotic music and test your knowledge of this American holiday by taking....

Dale's American Flag Exam

1. Who made the first American flag?

   a) Betsy Ross

   b) Ross Perot

   c) Martini & Rossi

2. How many white stars are on the flag?

   a) 50

   b) 13

   c) More white stars than you will find in the NBA.

3. Flagpole sitting was popular in:

   a) The 1920's

   b) Areas with a severe chair shortage.

   c) Gay bars.

4. A popular nickname for the flag is:

   a) Old Glory

   b) The Stars and Stripes

   c) Lenny

5. If you see the flag flying upside down it is an international sign of:

   a) Distress

   b) Stupidity

   c) Dyslexia

6. The proper way for a civilian to salute the flag is:

   a) Place your hand over your left breast

   b) Place your hat over your left breast

   c) Cover your hand with your hat and place it on someone else's breast.

16

Hut One, Hut Two, Hut-Choo - Gesundheit

I love football. It is a wonderful sport where genetically enhanced behemoths crash into each other with crushing force while we get to sit at home and drink beer. Gee, the days of the ancient Roman gladiators must have really been something. But the difference between football and fighting lions is that football has rules. The question is, do you know those rules?

I think we all know that a touchdown is 6 points and five touchdowns equals an athletic shoe endorsement, but are we clear on the other rules? Recent surveys point out that 75% of alleged football FANS do not know their hip pads from a hole in the ground when it comes to real football terminology. In the case of TV football ANNOUNCERS, the number is 95%. If this is the huddle into which you fall, this is your lucky day.

In order to make the American people more pigskin prolific, I am proud to present...

Dale's Football Footnotes

PASS - An introduction to courtship as in, "Hey, pal, are you making a pass at my wife?"

KICKOFF - A term used to describe the consequences facing a player caught violating team rules, as in, "Leroy be kickoff the team for doin' heroin."

BLITZ - A tasty pastry usually served after the game with tea. The cheese blitzes are especially good with sour cream.

CLIPPING - What must be done to the grass around

the edges of the playing field in order to maintain a neat and tidy appearance.

DEAD BALL- A medical term for that portion of a player's anatomy which has ceased to function due to a nasty hit.

INTENTIONAL GROUNDING- Not allowing a player to leave his room for a month because he was bad.

TOUCHBACK - Similar to a tag back. During the course of a game, players will touch each other on the rear ends and then declare "No Touchbacks." It's wacky gridiron fun.

WAIVERS - Fans who will do anything to get on camera.

DEFENSE - A barrier surrounding the stadium.

PENETRATION - Usually the result of a successful PASS, this move is favored by players playing on the road.

SACK - Where the penetration usually takes place.

TWO MINUTE WARNING- Given towards the end of the penetration.

17

Beer, Beer,
The Musical Fruit

There is one time of the year when I think about beer more than I normally do...which is often. Oktoberfest, held annually in September to confuse the public, is a celebration of the ancient art of brewing beer. While Oktoberfest originates in Germany, we in America are always on the lookout for an excuse to drink beer even though American beer can not hold a bottle opener to its German cousin.

This is a time to concentrate on the QUALITY of American beer as opposed to concentrating on the QUANTITY as we normally do. Now I do not think it is abnormal to consume six to eight beers a day but then I don't think it is abnormal to use a Chihuahua as a door stop. A lot of people may disagree with me...especially the MADH (Mothers Against Drunk Husbands) and people who own Chihuahuas. But I say heck with them.

It is every American's God given right to suck back a cool and frosty brew every so often just as long as you don't bother anyone else by being rude or throwing up on them. If you agree with me, then you believe in drinking responsibly. And for those who are unfamiliar with the concept of drinking responsibly, I am proud to present...

Dale's 6-Pack Of Beer Drinking Rules

1. **Never drink beer alone.** This will brand you as someone with a drinking problem, plus it is darn near impossible to get anyone to buy you a free drink if there is no one there.

2. **Pee responsibly**. It is no secret that beer goes through you faster than a Democrat goes through tax money but this is no excuse to ignore proper elimination etiquette. First of all, ALWAYS LIFT UP THE SEAT...no matter where you are. Although beer drinkers like to pride themselves on their accuracy, nobody hits the bulls-eye every time. If the seat will not stay up, feel free to use the shower, just try to avoid doing so if someone is already in there. Also, if you are at an outdoor function which does not have adequate facilities, it is OK to resort to backwoods techniques. Just try to avoid going in the middle of open pastures or on a highway median strip. Remember the old adage, "When you take a leak, be discrete."

3. **Never buy beer based on their TV commercials.** I know a lot of you are swayed towards one brand or another by their glitzy and glamorous commercials. It's hard to resist buying a beer endorsed by talking frogs or a washed up has-been athlete but this just isn't right. To the real beer drinker, the beer of choice is more than a well produced TV ad...it's the one that's on sale.

4. **Waste not want not.** This old aphorism was never truer than when applied to beer. Beer was meant for drinking, not cooking, shampooing, or removing rust from car bumpers. It was also not meant to be used as a bait to catch slugs although many sicko gardeners swear that it works.

Above all, beer should never be used for locker room celebrations. Nothing sickens me more than the thought of good beer being sprayed around a victorious locker room like a fire hose at a riot. Don't waste your beer this way. This is what sissy champagne was made for.

5. **Accept no substitutes.** A few years ago some pea brain came up with the idea of LOW ALCOHOL BEER. Then, recently, some other cretin invented NO ALCOHOL BEER. Hey guys, what's your point? They claim that their brews have "retained the great beer taste but removed the alcohol." Excuse me? First of all, beer does not taste that great. In fact, it tastes like a dear toad smells...especially imported beers that rhyme with Byniken. We drink beer for one reason only...the BUZZ. If you are going to take the buzz out of beer, you might as well take the orgasm out of sex. Without it, it's just a waste of time.

6. **Don't drink and drive.** This one is serious. If you are going to drink, have somebody else drive you home. Or, better yet, crawl into a corner of the bar where you won't be noticed and can sleep undisturbed. Then, in the morning, you will be the first customer waiting to be served.

18

God, Even My Hair Hurts

We've all been there. You wake up in the morning and the sound of grass growing starts your head thumping like the Energizer Bunny's bass drum. Your mouth feels as if the Bolshoi ballet used it for a locker room. Your eyes will open but cannot focus. The entire room is expanding and contracting like it was hooked up to a huge respirator. Your stomach feels like the Bolivian militia used it for bayonet practice. You find yourself praying to God and promising to give all of your earthly possessions to the poor and live a life of monastic solitude if He will just make the hurt go away. You also wind up making the irrational promise of never drinking again. In short, YOU HAVE A HANGOVER.

Until now, hangovers received the lowest priority on the universal list of physical ailments. Hangovers were down there with paper cuts and zits on the sympathy poll. There was no cure, you received no sympathy, and worst of all, you were still expected to be at work. But now, thanks to some knuckleheads in Massachusetts with a lot of time on their hands, February 7th has been proclaimed National Hangover Awareness Day. Apparently, on this day, you are supposed to appreciate the hangover you received as a result of exceeding your alcohol consumption capacity on February 6th.

Now, while this may seem like another goofy PR stunt, it does raise a logical question. Exactly what can we do about hangovers? Well, my friends, I am happy that I can help you out in this area because in honor of this momentous occasion, I am proud to share my previously unreleased cures for the modern hangover. It is something I like to call...

Dale's Hangover Cures

1. Immerse yourself in a pool of luke warm rice pudding for six hours. Besides the pleasant feeling, the pudding will have a purgative effect on your body's toxins and will suck them right through your pores leaving you feeling clean and relaxed. If you do not happen to have access to a pool and/ or 300 gallons of rice pudding try...

2. A hair of the dog that bit you. Now I know we have all heard of this theory but I have given it a new twist. In my version, actually go out and have a dog bite you. I would suggest this be a smaller dog, perhaps something in the Poodle or Pekinese families. Being bitten by a Rottweiler or a Pit Bull could lead to more pain than the hangover you are trying to cure.

After the dog bites you, remove all of its hair with an electric shaver. Between the pain of the dog bite, and the laughter you will experience from staring at a bald dog, you will completely forget about your hangover.

3. Have your liver dry cleaned. This is a relatively simple procedure which requires a sharp knife, some paper towels, and a dry cleaner who delivers. Just remove your liver, wrap it in the paper towels, and have the dry cleaner pick it up for a fast one hour Martinizing job. When your liver returns, take it off of the hanger and place it back in your body where it will now operate at peak performance to clean out all of the bad liquor residue that is causing your discomfort.

IMPORTANT. Don't forget to remove the cleaner's

tag before you re-insert your organ. It could cause an infection and the staple holding it in place is bound to hurt.

4. Go down to the garage and start the car. Stay in the car with the windows rolled up and the garage door down until the pain goes away.

CAUTION, this cure is not recommended unless you have an electric car or a lot of life insurance which names me as the beneficiary. This remedy, however, does aid you in fulfilling that promise you made to God about never drinking again.

19

Just Wait 'Till Your Father Gets Home

Father's Day is a time for dads across the country to get the short end of the stick. Think about it. On Mother's Day, mom gets flowers, presents, and a fancy meal at a restaurant. On Father's Day dad usually gets an ugly tie, a box of cheap cigars, and the responsibility for barbecuing the family's meal on the Weber grill which he has never learned to master so that all of the expensive steaks wind up looking like something which requires dental charts to recognize. It isn't fair.

This year, in order to help you truly show your appreciation for your dad, I have undertaken extensive research to determine the top presents that dads do and don't want on Father's Day. Well, it wasn't actually extensive research, seeing as how I only asked four guys down at the liquor store and the guy that delivers the weekly shopper newspaper. But here are the results of my findings anyway.

The Top Ten Things Dads Don't Want For Father's Day

10. Any article of clothing with an alligator on it.

9. Anything which has to be assembled.

8. An autographed picture of Regis Philbin.

7. Socks.

6. Underwear, especially those skimpy European bikini ones that dad calls "Faggy little nut huggers."

5. Tickets to see the opera.

4. Tickets to see Oprah.

3. A plunger/sewer-snake combination ensemble.

2. Any cologne that isn't Old Spice or Aqua Velva.

1. And the number one thing that dads do NOT want for Father's Day...a subpoena for vagrancy.

Now, I know you are saying, "OK Mr. Wise Guy, now that you have told us what our dads don't want for Father's Day, how about telling us what they want?" Well kids, when it comes to enjoyable Father's Day gifts that will be remembered for a lifetime, you can limit your present selection to the following: TOYS, POWER TOOLS, PICTURES OF NAKED BABES, PICTURES OF NAKED BABES HOLDING POWER TOOLS. It's that easy, it's that simple.

20

Equus, Schmekwus, My Ass Hurts

One summer I had an experience which I hope to never repeat. While vacationing in the mountains of Pennsylvania (Land of Inbreeding) I was coerced into trying a sport which in my opinion ranks right up there with luge riding or rollerball in the potential-for-injury category. I am referring to horseback riding.

Oh, I can just see you all now calling me a sissy and a weenie city boy, but before ye judge, let me fill you in on the dark side of this equine hell.

My previous equestrian experience consisted of pony rides at the local carnival. This is where you rest on the back of a luded out Shetland who is tethered to a rotating device that confines him to going round and round in a circle all day without going anywhere. This device is called the Halter of Congress. Anyhow, this was my only horse experience so what came next was an event for which I was not properly prepared.

At the stable, the horses were paraded out for all of the customers to view and photograph. Then, they were assigned to each rider by a semi-toothless man named Skeeter. "All righty, the little girl there gets Molasses. The lady with the big chi-chis gets Lazy Boy, the man with the pocket protector gets Buttercup, and you sir (pointing at me) you get SATAN'S LOVE CHILD." With that, a huge devil of a horse was brought out of the stable breathing smoke and bearing the brand 666. "Don't be afeered of him now son", Skeeter was telling me, "He ain't kilt nobody in nye over a week now." CHECK PLEASE. Even though I knew this son of his own cousins was joking with me, I really wasn't ready for this adventure. But before I knew it, I was being boosted up on the beast's back and was instructed on the mechanics of horse steering.

A few tips for you in this area if you ever decide to attempt this sport. First, the horn on the saddle does not work. Perhaps mine needed new batteries but I couldn't get I single beep out of it. Second, the reins mean nothing. Horses will go wherever they want to go and your constant tugging on the leather strips affixed to their orthodontic appliance will only tick them off. You can tell when your horse is getting upset with your rein handling because he will turn his head around and look at you while saying in horse talk, "Hey Stupid, that hurts. Don't tug on those things again or I will crush you like a grape."

Finally, never kick a horse to get him to go faster. Kicking a horse to go faster is like telling an Armenian cab driver to "Step on it." Horses (and Armenians) know only two speeds, very slow, and way too fast. Always opt for slow. I made the mistake of nudging my nag to increase the speed ever so slightly and was rewarded with a bouncing exhibition of horsepower which caused both fear and pain. It caused fear because I thought for sure that this mentally disturbed animal was going to run out in traffic with me on his back and scream "Somebody hit me, life isn't worth living anymore." And it caused pain because the male genitalia do not take kindly to being slapped against a hard leather saddle like so many ping pong balls in a lotto machine.

BULLETIN - IF YOU ARE A MAN, NEVER GO HORSEBACK RIDING WITHOUT A STEEL CUP.

To make a horror story short, Satan's Love Child and I eventually reached an agreement whereby I would not tug on his bridle, nor would I attempt to alter the direction of his chosen path. In return, he vowed to let me live. At the conclusion of the ride, the other members of the party were laughing and singing rodeo songs while I was checking my personal parts inventory and vomiting profusely.

The moral of the story is thus - If God would have wanted us to ride horses, He would have shaped them like easy chairs.

21

Romance Rhymes With Underpants

A friend recently gave me a copy of a book which proves that there is a market for darn near everything. The name of the book is "1001 Ways To Be Romantic" by Gregory J. P. Godek. Right off the bat you have got to question the romantic expertise of some guy with two middle initials.

If you are going to be romantic, you should select a romantic name like James Bond who has no middle initials; Casanova, who doesn't even have a last name; or Wilt "The Stilt" Chamberlain who has two middle names but at least has the common sense to use them in toto.

This was a good move on his part because Wilt T.S. Chamberlain would have made him sound like some sort of intellectual whereas "The Stilt" spelled out the fact that he is more like a throbbing aneurysm of testosterone.

Finally, the writer could have adopted the ultimate romantic name of John Smith, a name used by thousands of romantics at motel registrations over the years. But I do not wish to belabor the author's choice of bylines, I would rather critique his book.

"1001 Ways To Be Romantic" gives you little tips to show your loved one how you feel about them. That's what it claims to do. In reality, it gives you tips on how to grease the skids for an evening of naked slam dancing. Some of the tips offered in the book include:

* Name your boat after her.

* Watch a Leo Buscalia video tape together.

* Sit in front of a fireplace with a roaring fire.

* Wash her hair.

This list goes on and on 1001 times. I don't mean to doubt the author's expertise on the subject of romance but some of his ideas are just plain goofy. I can understand the boat naming and the hair washing ideas but the only way to watch a Leo Buscalia video tape is by tossing it into the roaring fire and seeing what kind of colored flames it generates.

If you are one of those incurable romantics, I suggest that you pick up this book and follow some of its guidelines. Who knows, they may work for you. The problem is that once you start down this path of romance you will be EXPECTED TO BE ROMANTIC ALL OF THE TIME! She will expect you to top each day's romantic gesture with one that is even more romantic. This is nuts. By the end of a month you will find yourself having to spend most of your bowling money on flowers and Hallmark cards. I suggest that you plan your romantic adventures with a taste of realism in mind.

That is why I have constructed the following list of romantic tips which will not cause a significant change in your lifestyle but will still accomplish the same end result. I prefer to think of it as Romance Lite.

Dale's Tips For Romance

1. Write "I Love You" in the dust on the coffee table.

2. Refrain from drinking milk right out of the carton for an entire day.

3. Next time you go out to dinner, let HER talk to the person at the drive-thru.

4. Tell her she can use the remote control for an entire evening. Then, go bowling.

5. Buy her a new can of Ajax for no reason at all.

6. Go outside to burp.

7. Buy a subscription to Playboy in her name.

8. The next time you stay in a hotel on business, stop by the maid's cart and bring home some shampoo, conditioner, and a shower cap. If you really want to impress her, take home a set of freshly laundered sheets as well.

9. Put her picture on the refrigerator. Or, better yet, tape it to the milk carton. This is not only romantic, but it will keep her on her toes.

10. Name your lawn mower after her.

Just follow these tips and Romance will be your middle name.

22

A Chapter With Bite

by Eddie Lubitsch, The Last Angry Man

I hate dentists. I would never say this to one while I was strapped in his chair but orthodontists really floss my flukes. You are probably wondering what brought on this uncalled for tirade. Well I'll tell you.

It all started when I read that September 13th marks the start of Dental Awareness Week in America. What the heck kind of a deal is this? Is there a man, woman, or child in this country that is not aware of dentists? Even MY DOG had to visit a dentist. She had a problem with her canine teeth. Ha, ha, ha.

Recently I had to visit the dentist too. I didn't want to but I was experiencing pain every time I ate, drank, or swallowed so I figured I had better get it checked out. Make no bones about it, on the pain scale a trip to the drill doctor ranks right up there with an IRS audit or the time I tried to ride my bicycle without a seat.

Everything about a visit to the dentist is painful, from being forced to read those magazines dating back to the Eisenhower administration, to gagging on those x-ray plates that you are told to "Bite down on".

Nonetheless, I recently booked an appointment with Dr. Blackendecker to check into my molar anguish. I worried about the potential pain night and day. Then it dawned on me and I said to myself, "Hey Eddie, why don't you MAKE SURE that this visit is painless." So I set out a plan.

On the morning of the fateful appointment, I woke up and fixed a pitcher of Bloody Marys for breakfast. Then I had Estelle drive me to Ye Olde Dental Torture Chamber, stopping for a couple of beers along the way. By the time we got there I was feeling no pain at all.

Once in the dentist's office, I slurred my name to the receptionist and she showed me to my chair. She asked if I needed anything and I said, "Yeah, how about a hickie?" She smacked me with a National Geographic but guess what? IT DIDN'T HURT.

Next, in walked Dr. Doom who asked me where the pain was. I said "In my mouth, Doc" and proceeded to laugh hysterically. He probed for a while and told me he was going to give me some nitrous oxide. I didn't know what it was but agreed anyhow. ATTENTION. WHEN YOU GO TO THE DENTIST, ASK FOR NITROUS OXIDE. BETTER YET, INSIST ON IT. This oxide stuff is the greatest thing since whipped cream. This odorless gas makes you loopy, and when used in conjunction with Bloody Marys and beer, makes you bulletproof.

Next came the shot of Novocain to numb my tooth. Great idea. I was now not only bulletproof, but I was drooling too. After ten minutes my body was desensitized to the point where I felt like it was constructed of tapioca pudding. Needless to say, the rest of the visit proceeded with no pain on my part. There was, however, one major problem to my pain avoidance plan. While I achieved my state of numbness one step at a time, I did not regain my normal sensations in the same manner. In fact all of my pain killers WORE OFF AT ONCE.

I went from being a pain free tapioca boy to a creature who's every sense was back, and highly alert. Now I was not only in great pain but also hung over. So I have learned my lesson. Next time....bring aspirin!

And it's lessons learned too late in life that make me, The Last Angry Man.

That's all from me....for now.

23

Dinner Will Be Ready In 60 Seconds

I don't know about you but I remember the good old days when it took mom all day to cook the evening meal. She would slave over the stove for hours making vegetables, potatoes, bread, more potatoes, dessert, potatoes, and a pot roast you could chew for a week. Mmmm, mmmmm, that was good eatin'.

But nowadays nobody spends any time in the kitchen. Everything is instant. Instant meat, instant potatoes, and instant indigestion, all thanks to the boon of mankind, the MICROWAVE OVEN. This electronic Pandora's Box has reduced the culinary art form to the pressing of a few buttons. To me, this is like covering the ceiling of the Sistine Chapel with wallpaper.

This all comes to light in October which has been proclaimed National Microwave Month and it prompts me to ask the question, "Do we need microwaves at all?" These modern conveniences have been more of a burden on society than a help. It used to be that you could look forward to sipping a cup of FRESH BREWED coffee when you woke up each morning. But thanks to the jiffy cooker you simply pop a cup of yesterday's java in the microwave, nuke it for a few seconds, and prepare to slurp some freshly reheated sludge. In my mind, there are other household appliances more deserving of having their own month.

How about National Electric Can Opener Month? This handy device has made it possible to open a can of tomato soup and a can of dog food in under 30 seconds IMPARTING THE FLAVOR OF THE DOG

FOOD TO THE SOUP. I don't know about you but there is nothing I look forward to more than a cup of piping hot Campbell's tomato soup with a delicate essence of Alpo.

Maybe we should salute the Hot Air Popcorn Popper, a convenience which allows us to cook up a batch of popcorn which contains no fat, no oil, and no taste. Air popped popcorn has a similarity to hot Styrofoam. Why don't they just make a Hot Styrofoam Maker for either tasty snacks or for packing delicate objects.

Personally, I think we should have a month set aside to honor the VACU-PACKER. This is a gadget that I bought from the Home Shopping Network one night when I thought vodka and Gatorade was a good idea. The VACU-PACKER sucks all of the air out of a plastic bag containing your leftovers. This accomplishes two things. First, it creates a vacuum in the bag so that the food will stay fresh through the next millennium, and second, it gives you a cool new toy to play with after dinner. I especially enjoy drawing a face on a ripe peach, then putting it in a bag and sucking the air out until the tiny little fruit head collapses. It's great therapy.

But, none of this is going to happen in the near future so we are stuck with National Microwave Month. To celebrate I suggest that you construct little people out of cheese sticks and put the brave little gladiators in the microwave arena. Set it on high, and watch 'em melt.

Who says cooking can't be fun.

24

Does Anybody Really Know What Time It Is?

This has been the perennial question asked ever since... well, ever since the group Chicago asked it in their 1967 hit of the same name which contained the meaningful lyrics:

Does anybody really know what time it is?
Does anybody really care?
Though I can't imagine why,
We all have time enough to die.

What the heck kind of crap is this? We all have time enough to die? Like dying is going to take that much time out of your day. I don't think so. One second you're here and then BINGO, you're history. Anyway, rock lyrics of the sixties are not really the topic of this chapter. Time is.

As you probably know by now, we have to reset our clocks twice a year to accommodate the invention of Daylight Savings Time. Unfortunately, I never know whether to set my clocks ahead or back. So I have to rely on that old adage, Spring AHEAD, Fall on your BACK. That means that TECHNICALLY, we should gain an hour in the Spring and I want to know where it went!

I have nothing to show for this extra hour. I didn't get to watch an extra hour of TV. I didn't get an extra hour of sleep. I didn't even get an extra hour of making love...not that I could make it last for an hour but that's not important. What is important is that I spent my extra hour resetting ALL of my clocks. I started with my watch, or watches actually, because when I was in New York I found it easier to buy a watch from a street corner entrepreneur every day than to wear a good watch thus inviting a mugger to slice off my arm to steal it. From there, I reset my alarm clock, my kitchen clock, my dining room clock, and the clock in the horse's stomach that sits on my mantel.

With all of those clocks reset, I moved on to the more complicated time keepers. The clock in my car needed to be reset as did the one on the microwave.

Then came the clocks on the stove, the VCR, (yes, some people actually SET these clocks), and the one built into the television. I continued with every light timer in the house and the little clock inside my answering machine that time stamps my calls. By the time I finished with all of this resetting, I was exhausted. SO there went my extra hour...and when Spring comes I will both lose an hour and WILL HAVE TO WASTE ANOTHER HOUR setting all of my time pieces AHEAD. I have a better idea.

Instead of fiddling around with our concept of time, the U.S. Government Department of Precision Minutes and Seconds, or PMS, should consider the following:

1. When we set our clocks back in the fall, it suddenly gets dark at 3:30 in the afternoon. This stinks.

2. Therefore, if we didn't set our clocks back in the fall, it would stay light longer.

3. If we continued to set our clocks AHEAD in the spring, we would wind up with a time surplus.

4. At the end of 24 years, we would have built up a surplus of 24 hours or ONE WHOLE DAY.

5. This day could then be used by those of us who at one time or another thought, "Gee, I wish I had today to live over again."

6. OR, this extra day could be used for a nationwide holiday where EVERY SINGLE BUSINESS would be closed. It wouldn't hurt anybody's business because this day wouldn't even show up on a calendar. IT'S A FREE DAY.

7. Therefore, every American, during an average lifetime, could expect to receive THREE FREE DAYS from the US government which beats the hell out of free cheese. Call me nuts but this makes sense.

So I urge you friends, write to your congressman... I'm sorry, CONGRESSPERSON, because a good idea like this should not go to waste. Who knows, with all of the new people in the legislature, it might confuse them enough to actually get passed.

25

A Rose Is A Rose
Is A Girl's Name

Lately I've been thinking a lot about names. Just last night I was watching American Gladiators and I thought to myself, "Gosh, these guys have cool names". If you have never seen the show, the male steroid users on the program have names like Thunder, and Typhoon, and their female counterparts have monikers like Diamond, and Ice. All I know is that they are darned lucky to have landed the jobs they did.

With a vanilla name like Dale, I could pretty much be anything from a comedian to a guy who works behind the counter at Dairy Queen. But with a name like Typhoon, you are relegated to a life as an American Gladiator. I mean, who's going to buy life insurance from somebody named after a natural disaster? The same is true for women, although I think Diamond and Ice make nice names for hookers as well as gladiators.

But all that aside, this little venture into the nomenclature field got me to thinking about something. Guys have received the muddy end of the stick when it comes to names. Take a look at women's names. They all sound nice and feminine like Mary, or Judy, or Lucretia. They all sound melodical but best of all, THEY DON'T HAVE DOUBLE MEANINGS.

Girl's names all mean only one thing...the name of the girl possessing the name. But guy's names can also stand for other often unsavory terms in the English language. Take RALPH for instance. Sure it is a guy's name but it also means TO THROW UP, as in

"I'm going to RALPH". And this is not an isolated instance.

Poor JOHN has had to suffer through eons of sharing his name with the common toilet. And over in Great Britain, LOU has a similar problem, although they spell their toilet "Loo" but a homonym is a homonym I always say.

In Autumn, it is very popular to BOB for apples, while on the first of every month we dread having to receive BILLS in the mail. How many of you have walked into a neighborhood diner and ordered a hot cup of JOE to start your day or sauntered into a tavern and asked for a cold BUD?

When somebody tries to ROB you they usually JIMMY open the door, and if you catch them and they shoot you. Well, I just hope your WILL is up to date.

Be careful where you park your car because a careless person might put a NICK in your door or steal your gas after you just PHILed the tank. I am being very FRANK and EARNEST with you.

When you go to the doctor he might have to LANCE your boil or place you in a sick WARD. And, he'll charge you a lot of money so that he can get RICH.

It's all so unfair. Men who exercise need to wear a JACQUES strap so if they get RANDY they won't display a WOODY. And you don't even want to think about the poor saps named PETER, DICK, and WILLY.

So wake up men and demand your rights. Demand the right to Freedom Of Name so that if you feel your name is being made a mockery of you can change it to something which has no double entendre. Who's with me? Come on, let's see a show of HANS.

26

Do You Smell That?

From our Department Of Current But Irrelevant Events comes this choice tidbit of crucial information. According to a Yale University research project, we, as humans, are able to identify some smells more readily than others.

After testing over 200 people, the Yale smell doctors determined that the most recognizable aroma to the average person is COFFEE. This was followed by peanut butter, Vicks VapoRub, and chocolate. Cigarette butts came up 7th on the list, tuna showed up 16th, and crayons were in the 18th position. Now, granted, I can't speak for everyone, but I think the Yalies have missed the smell boat by a fathom or two.

In keeping with their button down Ivy League tradition, I don't think they included some of the more pungent and possibly offensive smells in their survey. So I conducted a survey of my own to get to the real core of the smell business.

I surveyed six people who happened to ring my doorbell last week. Three of them were political candidates, two were selling candy, and one was a Jehovah's Witness. I invited them all to sniff a variety of scents that one might find in your average home and at the conclusion of my research I found that my results varied greatly from those collected by Yale.

The most recognizable smells in order of their recognizability were:

1. Wet Dog

2. Garbage

3. Old Tennis Shoes

4. Minnow Bucket

5. Some Stuff That I Found In My Refrigerator That Used To Be Chicken

In light of this exhaustive and thorough research, I hope the folks at Yale take another look at their findings. If they like, they can call me and I will be happy to share my data with them because science marches on.

27

Oh Tannenbaum,
Oh Grease My Palm

The headline of this chapter means nothing. All it does is rhyme, and it is not that easy to rhyme anything with Tannenbaum, which is why it is not one of our more popular Christmas carols.

Tannenbaum, in case you were not aware of it, is the German word for Christmas tree. While we are on the subject, Genseklein is the German word for goose giblets and Bremsbelag is the German word for brake lining. BUT, do you know the German word for photo finish? It's PHOTOFINISH. Ha, ha, ha, those wacky Germans. They love to play linguistic pranks.

But back to the business of Tannenbaums. The Christmas season (which extends from Labor Day to Christmas) is a time of year when traditionalists like to chop down a living tree and haul it into their home to dry out. Then, they hang hot lights from the branches to suck out any remaining mosture.

Non-traditionalists, on the other hand, prefer artificial trees made out of substances with which one would normally make either cookware or toilet brushes. Well I say, "The heck with these people." The only real way to celebrate the Christmas season is to kill a real tree.

Ever since Halloween, vacant lots across America have been turned into faux forests with the display of hundreds of Christmas trees. These trees were cut down in July and shipped in September so that we could buy them in December and wonder why all of the needles fell off before January.

But here is the real kicker. The same Christmas

trees that used to cost five bucks when you were a kid now cost, are you ready for this, ONE HUNDRED DOLLARS! OK, so maybe they are not the SAME trees, but the point of the matter is that over the last 25 years, the cost of Christmas trees has gone through the roof.

Something has to be done about this spiraling Yuletide inflation and it is a good thing for you that I am here to do it. In the true spirit of the season, I have prepared some tips on how you can provide a Christmas tree for your family without going broke. I call them.....

Dale's Tips On Buying A Christmas Tree Without Going Broke

1. **Avoid evergreens.** Almost everyone you meet wants to use a fir, pine, or spruce tree for their holiday decorating. This kind of supply and demand is what drives up the price. Instead, opt for a nice dead maple or oak. These trees are in ready abundance across the land and they can be had dirt cheap. Oh, sure, a dead maple may need to be trimmed since they usually grow to about 30 or 40 feet, but you can use everything you trim off of it to make a nice wreath or some dandy furniture. Also, you don't have to worry about cleaning up pesky needles since these deciduous beauties will be as naked as strippers and with fewer bugs on them.

2. **Shop late.** The best bargains are to be had around December 26th. At this time you can pick up the tree of your choice for a song...even if you don't sing very well. Oh, I know what you are saying, you think that December 26th is too late to get a tree because Christmas was on December 25th. Hey, I know that and you know that, but your

neighbors don't know that. I am suggesting that you buy the biggest tree you can find on the 26th, bring it home, and toss it on your front lawn. The neighbors will be very impressed that you could afford such an expensive tree and will look at you with renewed respect. And what did it cost you? Maybe a buck and a half tops.

3. **Buy in bulk.** Team up with your neighbors and friends to buy your trees in large quantities. Then, you can go down to the local tree lot and say, "I'll give you a grand for all of 'em!" The local tree lot guy will probably be floored at such an offer and say, "What?" At this point, you peel off 10 hundred dollar bills, stick them in the tree lot guy's pocket and start hauling away your trees. Since tree lot guys are notoriously poor at mathematics, which is why they are tree lot guys and not accountants, they will not realize that you bought all of their trees for an average price of three dollars each until the next day. By then, you, and the trees, have disappeared.

4. **Buy a live tree.** Instead of dragging a pine corpse into your living room, invest in a real live tree. You can still decorate it and put presents under it, but after the holidays it will still live and grow. The only problem here is that in a couple of years you might have to remove a portion of your roof because these things grow fast and require a lot of light.

5. **Tape it.** Since we are convinced that a real tree is the only way to go, you may want to consider having the most beautiful tree in town. I am referring to the municipal tree that your city will put up on the town square and spend thousands of hours and dollars decorating. These trees are always gorgeous. To bring this tree into your home, all

you have to do is set up your video camera and tape the tree for two hours (six hours if you use SLP). Then, bring the tape home, plug it into the VCR, and you have a real tree, all decorated, with no cleanup to worry about. And the best part...after the holidays you can reuse the tape for those Gilligan's Island reruns you love so much.

28

It's America's Game

When John Naismith invented basketball in 1891 I doubt that he ever expected it to become this country's number one sporting event. In fact, I am sure he never expected it or he would have invested more heavily in Nike stock. But poor foresight aside, Naismith's game is responsible for a large portion of our sports attention. With that in mind, I thought that it would be important for us all to have a little better understanding of the game.

Without further ado, I am pleased to present a spectators' guide to the world of basketball.

Dale's Guide To Professional Basketball

Basketball is a game played on a court 94 feet long and 50 feet wide, or is it the other way around? Suffice it to say that it is played on a rectangle. This rectangle is surrounded by high rollers who have enough surplus income to be able to afford upwards of $250 for a seat in a folding chair. Painted on the rectangle are a series of lines. These lines are defined as follows:

Center Line - This would be the one in the middle, duhhhh.

Base Line - This is the music played by the low string instrument in the group. Some say it should be spelled "bass line" but that is the music played by the low fish in the group (see "scales").

Free Throw Line - This is the only place on the court where it is OK for a player to throw up.

Three Point Line - Any shots made from behind this

line are worth three points. Any shots missed from behind this line are still worth nothing. Hence, a player is only rewarded for success and not for attempting. Are these the kind of values we should be teaching the children?

A game of basketball consists of four periods, each of which is 12 minutes long. Professional basketball does not comply with the time-space continuum since a single 12 minute period can contain over 20 minutes of TV commercials.

After two periods have been played, all action is stopped for half-time. Half time is a 20 minute window of opportunity for those with a desire to watch a dog chase a Frisbee or some other sterling half time entertainment package. Those of us watching the game on TV have more limited half time options consisting of going to the bathroom and getting some snacks. Half-time is followed by the exciting third and fourth periods. The fourth period is my personal favorite. If anything really exciting is going to happen in the game, it is going to happen in the last two minutes. This is also true of sex.

Each player is allowed to smack the players on the other team five times. These events of physical contact are called fouls. A player is allowed to have five fouls but on the sixth one he has to leave the game. I think this is unfair to the player and boring to the fan. If I had invented basketball I would allow a player as many fouls as he wants, but, for every one after five he has to take a punch in the face from the other team's head coach. But, I didn't invent the game so we are stuck with Mr. Naismith's rules. Since there are so many different kind of fouls, I thought it would be a good idea to explain each.

Personal Foul - This is a foul committed by one player upon another player.

Impersonal Foul - This is a foul committed by one player upon a total stranger that he has never seen before.

Madrigal Foul - This is a foul committed by one player against a group of singers. It is rarely called.

Technical Foul - This is a foul called against a player who is "technically" doing something wrong. A technical foul could be called against a player who does not high five other players after a good shot; or any player who is playing in shoes which are not the same brand he endorses.

Flagrant Foul - This foul is committed on purpose and with intent to injure. It should never be confused with the Fragrant Foul which is committed by a player wearing too much cologne.

Loose Ball Foul - This foul is called against a player for not wearing a jock strap.

Basically, basketball is the simple exercise of putting a ball through a hoop. This can be accomplished in many different ways via different "shots".

Set Shot - The player is standing still, or "set" as he releases the ball.

Jump Shot - The player is jumping as he releases the ball.

Hook Shot - Player is soliciting a prostitute as he releases the ball.

Free Throw - A shot, which no matter how beautiful it is, cannot be used by a player as a means of raising his salary.

Dunk - A shot with a very high rate of success.

Ali Oop - A combination pass and dunk performed in mid air.

Muhammed Ali Oops- When an ex-heavyweight champ belches in public.

    I hope this new found knowledge of the game brings you a renewed appreciation of professional basketball. Next time I hope we can discuss why pro basketball players have such goofy names

29

Humbug!

By Eddie Lubitsch,
The Last Angry Man

I hate the holidays. I hate that interminably long period from Halloween to New Year's that descends upon us every year like a vulture on carrion. And the thing I hate most about it is that it never lets up.

Start with Halloween. this formerly innocuous celebration featuring tikes dressed up as ghosts and goblins has exploded into a full blown holiday with outdoor decorations, holiday cards, and Halloween parties that rival presidential inaugurations. It's nuts. It has gotten so bad in my neighborhood that people celebrate Halloween WEEK complete with prizes for the most ghoulish yard decorations.

THEN, with Halloween hardly cold in the ground, we start to see Christmas decorations popping up all over. It's three weeks until Thanksgiving and the store displays have replaced Frankenstein with Frankincense but, I can deal with that since I never much liked the traditional Thanksgiving decorations anyhow. I mean, how much can you do with a Pilgrim, an Indian, and a beheaded turkey?

Before you know it, Thanksgiving comes and goes leaving us with what has become known as the "Holiday Shopping Season". This is a period of approximately three weeks when we pack ourselves into stores like so many sardines in a can, and buy overpriced baubles for our loved ones which they return to the store for cash later on.

Next on the holiday hit parade is Chanukah or Hanukkah, a holiday which is celebrated for eight days; four for each spelling. This is followed by Christmas or Hristmas which is celebrated both on Christmas Eve and Christmas Day, depending upon when your family likes to open the presents.

Christmas always used to be followed by a week off before we had to dive into New Year's but now there is some new holiday called Kwanzaa, a holiday which is worth 17 points in Scrabble PLUS a 50 point bonus for using all seven tiles. THEN, we finally have New Year's Eve, a night when normally sane people try to drink as much as the rest of us. This is followed by a period of vomiting, after which comes New Year's Day, a day dedicated to football.

SO, you can see why I am sick of the holidays. There are just too darn many of them in a short eight week period. I say, stretch them out a little bit so that we have something to do for the entire year. Move Christmas to July when it's warm enough to ride the new bicycle you got as a gift. Split up Chanukah into two holidays celebrating the one spelled with a C in May and saving the one spelled with an H until September. And as for Kwanzaa, I say move it to February to fill the gap between Groundhog Day and Valentines Day.

But now, I have to go. Apparently I have spent too much time writing this chapter because according to my Hallmark pocket calendar, I have only a few days to prepare for Martin Luther King Day...and I haven't even bought my cards yet.

And it's last minute preparations like this that makes me The Last Angry Man.

That's all from me...for now.

30

Let's Go Down
To The Kegel Kourse

During the winter months, we all start to get mighty bored. The days are short, the weather is cold, and TV sucks. So, we turn to the world of sports for relaxation. Normal winter sports, however, require a great deal of patience, skill, and warm clothing. Because of this, I have never been a big fan of winter sports.

As a public service I have researched all of the winter sports options available and rated each on a system of 1 to 5 snowflakes. One snowflake is poor, and 5 is most excellent. Here are my findings.

CURLING ❋

This sport, if you can call it that, was invented in Canada by lonely Canadians. It is a game of skill, precision, and trying not to get so drunk that you fall down. In CURLING, one player slides a rock-like device down the ice with no particular target in mind. Then, he tries to hit the rock with an object that looks like a big iron tea pot that got sat upon by (fill in the name of your favorite really fat person or Marlon Brando here) . BUT, he has the help of two idiots with brooms who think that they can actually affect the speed and direction of the moving stone by tidying up in front of it with their brooms. It's a fun game to view if you have absolutely nothing else to do and somebody pays you ten bucks to watch them curl.

ICE FISHING ❋ ❋

This is one of the all time favorite winter sports around. When you ice fish, you walk out onto the middle of a lake, punch a hole in the ice, drop your line in the hole, and sit down until the fish bites. No casting, no trolling, no tangled lines, no getting a hook in your head from your friend in the front of the boat who just got a new reel and doesn't know how to use it, and best of all, NO MOSQUITOES. In a sense, Ice Fishing could also be called Fishing For Idiots because there is really no way you can screw it up. The only thing that keeps this sport from garnering a higher snowflake rating is the fact that if you do not dress properly you could freeze certain anatomical appendages which would later have to be removed.

HOCKEY ❄ ❄

Hockey is a winter hybrid of the Ice Capades and a gang fight. When playing hockey (or hockeying) the players get dressed up in big uniforms stuffed with padding, grab big sticks, and proceed to whup each other until the last player standing with at least two teeth is declared the winner. From time to time, they also smack a hard rubber disc with their sticks sending it towards another player's dental work at speeds of over 100 miles per hour.

ICE SKATING ❄

Hockey without the fights.

SLEDDING ❄ ❄ ❄

Sledding is an excellent winter sport in that it combines the best elements of several sports. It takes the skill of curling, the patience of ice fishing, the speed of ice skating, and, if you lose control of your sled and hit a tree, the same potential tooth loss as hockey. All it is missing is a way to look cool while you are doing it. Admit it, kids look cute on sleds but adults just look like big stuffed doofuses in down clothing. that's why adults who used to enjoy sledding as kids invented the adult version known as...

SKIING ❄ ❄ ❄

The best part about this sport is that it is played at big fancy ski resorts. Now I wouldn't strap on a pair of skis to save my life but I do appreciate sitting in the lodge with a hot buttered ski bunny. TIP: Always speak with a French accent.

BOWLING ❄ ❄ ❄ ❄ ❄

Bowling is the ultimate winter sport. It has excitement, it has rented shoes that thousands of people have put on their stinky old feet before you, and it has electric hand dryers. And on top of all this....IT'S INDOORS. What more can you ask for in a winter sport?

31

I Don't Want
Your Stinking Letter

by Eddie Lubitsch, The Last Angry Man

One thing I really hate about Christmas is that invariably, the Lubitsch family will receive at least one of those awful Christmas cards containing a mass produced letter informing you of the achievements and successes of the Gruber Family. You probably received a letter from a family with another name. The point of the matter is that these letters are all the same. They all reflect on the wonderful things that various family members have done in the past year. It's enough to make a grown man sick.

The people who send these letters have all had a wonderful year. "Bob has been promoted at work, Emily's pickles won first prize at the Lutheran Women's Auxiliary Picnic for the 4th year in a row, and the twins are both on the honor role at school." Who needs to listen to this kind of crap? Not me.

Whenever I get one of these letters, I am tempted to send a letter back telling these people about my year. It would not be nearly as wonderful as theirs, and neither would anybody else's. In fact, here is a sample of the letter I am sending out next year. Feel free to use it to send to the people on your list who send you one of their "wonderful" letters. Just remember to change the names first.

Dear Friends:

Boy, so much has happened to us this year that I am at a loss where to begin. Well, I didn't win the lottery again this year, (ha, ha) although the money would have certainly come in handy to pay off the credit card bills and the payment on the trailer we were forced to move into when we lost all of our money investing in a chain of Tofu-On-A-Stick family restaurants. Thanks for the tip Uncle Stu.

I am proud to say that the lawn has never looked better but I guess all of the dead pets we buried in the yard this summer has had a fertilizing effect. Who'd have guessed that it was the tainted water supply that was killing them.

The kids are doing well in school and are all learning a trade. Oops, I guess I forgot to mention that we have seven kids now. They're all Korean and we adopted them from that Sally Struthers commercial. It was sort of like the home shopping network. I gave the operator my credit card and via return mail came a covey of Koreans.

I've been told that I can keep my job at the car wash for another year if I promise to use my own towels...sort of a cut back I guess. BUT, my perks include free UNLIMITED car washes. That should come in handy if the police ever find the car again.

At least we've all been healthy. That is if you don't count the regular assortment of colds, flu, pyorrhea, cardio-vascular decay, distemper, anthrax, severe cramping, lumbago, gout, impotence, and the heartbreak of psoriasis. Thank goodness we haven't had anything serious.

Time to go now and put the Christmas pot pie in the oven. We are having both families over for the holidays and I definitely have to run out and buy more ammunition. Have a Happy New Year.

The Lubitsches

32

Get To Know Your Presidents

The third Monday in February is President's Day. This is important to know for two reasons. First, President's Day is a national holiday which means that you probably don't have to go to work. Second, if you do have to work, I guess it's not that important of a day.

President's Day used to be called Washington's Birthday until all of the other former presidents started complaining about having to work on their own birthdays. So, in its infinite wisdom, Congress decided to make Washington's birthday a day to honor all former presidents. This eliminated the need for an additional 40 national holidays. It also necessitated moving Washington's Birthday to accommodate a long weekend. This upset Washington who didn't really want his birthday moved every year but since he was dead at the time, Congress ignored his concerns.

Since President's Day now is intended to honor all of our past presidents, AND since most of us can't remember more than a hand full of past presidents by name, I thought it would be a good idea to present you with a presidential quiz to strengthen your knowledge of the men who have occupied the highest office in the land.

President's Day Quiz

1. Martin Van Buren was the 8th president and was most famous for,

a) Bringing indoor plumbing to the White House.

b) Signing a peace treaty with Antarctica.

c) Having a famous twin sister, Abigail Van Buren.

2. Abraham Lincoln's Gettysburg address was,

a) Written on the back of an envelope.

b) The first presidential speech covered by CNN.

c) 1365 S. Quaker Ave.

3. President Jimmy Carter's real first names were,

a) James Earl

b) Jim Bob

c) Goober Matthew

4. Why was the Hoover vacuum named after President Herbert Hoover?

a) It's strong and dependable.

b) It's reliable and long lasting.

c) It sucks.

5. Every president except for one was married. The unmarried president was,

a) James Buchanan

b) very happy

c) just in politics to meet babes.

6. The first chief executive without a beard was,

a) William Howard Taft

b) Franklin Delano Roosevelt

c) Hillary Rodham Clinton

7. The most memorable presidential campaign slogan was,

a) Keep Cool With Coolidge.

b) I Like Ike.

c) Washington....Like The City

8. When he's not in the Oval Office, you are most likely to find the president in,

a) the Rhomboid Room.

b) the Trapezium Toilet.

c) the Sphere of Influence

9. "The Mother of Presidents" is better known as,

a) Virginia

b) Ohio

c) A very sore woman named Vera.

10. George Bush pitched horseshoes and Eisenhower golfed, but what was the favorite pastime of Grover Cleveland?

a) Training the dog

b) Flogging the dolphin

c) Telling people that he owned a big city in Ohio.

33

News You Can't Use

Someone once asked notorious bank robber Willie Sutton why he robbed banks and he replied, "'Cause that's where the money is."

This was an interesting answer because it began with a contraction, ended with a preposition, and contained an incorrect verb tense.

What people ask me from time to time is why I read so many newspapers. And I tell them *"'Cause that's where the funny is."* If you want to make yourself laugh, all you have to do is pick up any daily newspaper and you will undoubtedly come across stories like the ones I found in the Chicago Tribune.

The first story concerns the predicament faced by some residents of Winfield, Illinois. Apparently the residents of Shinnecock Court think that their street name is the basis for ridicule and snickering by those who do not live on Shinnecock Court. They even point out in the article that the residents of Shinnecock Court pronounce their street name as SHINN-EH-COCK. That's too bad, because, like you, I have been reading this whole chapter and pronouncing it to myself as SHINEY-COCK. Apparently, that is just the type of mispronunciation they are trying to avoid. They are currently petitioning the city to have the name of their street changed. If this is the case, I would like to propose several suggestions for a new name.

How about BIG DICK PARKWAY, or possibly LOVE POLE LANE? The point is that you residents of SHINNECOCK COURT should count your blessings. Your street name is not that bad...considering it could have been a lot worse. You could be living on LITTLE SHINNECOCK COURT.

In a related story from the same paper but on a different day, the residents of Sexauer Avenue in Elgin, Illinois are also getting tired of the name of their street. I happen to like Sexauer Avenue because it reminds me of an old joke. A man phones up Mr. Sexauer's place of employment looking for him. Unfortunately, he misdialed and got a different company. When the receptionist answered the phone the man inquired, "Do you have a Sexauer there?". The receptionist replied, "Sexauer? Honey, we're luck if we get a coffee break."

I found another goofball news story in the Las Vegas Review-Journal. This article spoke of the problem being dealt with at the Sedgwick County Zoo in Wichita, Kansas. It appears that the 3 year old male Arabian camel named Tommy has been dealing with his onset of puberty in a different if not creative way.

Tommy is a young camel in love. The object of his affection was Hanna, a beautiful female camel with the biggest set of humps Tommy had ever seen. Tommy couldn't wait to show Hanna how much he loved her when it was determined that Hanna had a spinal defect that required zoo officials to put her to sleep. Tommy was heartbroken. He succumbed to depression and despair. He spent his days mired in a morass of ennui and self pity. He rarely spoke and didn't touch his food.

But one day Tommy awoke and discovered the fire hydrant located in his pen. It was a good looking fire hydrant. In fact, Tommy thought, "It was darn cute". So Tommy introduced himself to the hydrant by rubbing up against it and relieving himself of his loneliness, often several times a day.

Zoo officials are now considering moving the fire hydrant outside of Tommy's pen because they are concerned for the safety of any fireman who would have to use the hydrant to fight a fire. They fear that Tommy might object to sharing his new love and a fireman is no match for a horny hormone-crazed camel.

I think they should leave the hydrant in the pen but just have Tommy legally marry it. Soon enough he would leave the hydrant alone.

Sunny Today With A 20% Chance Of Melanoma

34

In summer it is very sunny so whatever you do, DO NOT LEAVE THE HOUSE! Forget about having poolside fun. Don't even think about playing baseball. And above all, FORGET ABOUT A TAN. "The summer sun is nothing but misery. If you get any on you, you will surely die." These are the paraphrased words of the U.S. Department of Sun Block, the very same people who have declared (this part is real) July 3 as National Stay Out Of The Sun Day. Oh, boy, more government intervention.

The people in charge (heretofore known as TPIC) have determined that the sun, Old Sol, the luminous heavenly orb, the giver of life, is BAD FOR US. In fact, they think it could kill us. Meanwhile, fast food hamburgers, rollerblades, and other things that could cause serious damage remain unchecked. I am inclined to grab TPIC by their pasty white cheeks and scream "Solar Discrimination."

The sun is not bad for us. It gives us daylight, among other things, and I have always found daylight to be very useful, especially when it's dark outside. The sun also gives us Sun City where old people can wrinkle, Sunday dinner where we eat until we become bloated, and, of course, Sun Yat-Sen who was some important Chinese guy. In other words, we cannot do with out the sun. We like its warmth, its light, and its ability to give even the palest people a glow that distinguishes them from druids who spend their entire existence in caves.

So, to help you get over your Solar-Phobia, I have

developed a list of safe tanning suggestions. I call them...

Dale's Safe Tanning Suggestions.

1. **Never sun tan naked**. This may seem like an intriguing adventure when you first think about it. Going to a nude beach; free from the encumbrances of a bulky swim suit; lots of naked babes with huge hooters. Sure, it may seem like a blissful outing but allow me to enlighten you. First of all, beautiful babes with big hooters do not go to nude beaches. They go to fancy yachts with guys named Todd and Gunther. The women who visit nude beaches are, for the most part, applying for jobs as extras in the next "Free Willy" movie. They are large cellulite-laden creatures who will hurt you if you refuse to rub Coppertone on them. Many times they are accompanied by equally ugly men eager to display their Gilloolys for all to see.

   The other downside of sunbathing naked is that a sunburn can really REALLY sting. If you expose one of your more tender and sensitive regions to the rays of the sun for too long, you could suffer immeasurable pain. This is not fun. It hurts, it's embarrassing, and above all, you can not even tell anybody why you can't come into work for a while.

2. **Always wear a hat**. Wearing a hat while sun bathing is considered very cool. It allows you to make your own fashion statement. A big sombrero, for instance, says that a person tends to be shy. A baseball cap, on the other hand, indicates a playful person. A baseball cap worn backwards indicates an aggressive or dyslexic person. And a baseball cap turned to the side is indicative of a stupid person who can easily be taken advantage of.

   In addition to their statement of fashion, a hat also

protects your head from the sun's more powerful rays. Since your head is usually the part of your body that is closest to the sun, it stands to reason that it will receive the most powerful rays. Protect your head and the rest of your body will thank you for it. If you find yourself at the beach without a hat, learn to improvise. Fashion a head covering out of your socks, the beer cooler, or that pair of discarded underpants that seems to be left on every beach. Oh sure, people will look at you and point, but at least your head won't get overheated and explode.

3. **Don't stay in the sun too long**. This is always a difficult factor to determine. Is 30 minutes enough; is eight hours too much? The answer to this puzzle can only be answered by you. Since every person is different only you can determine how much sun time you need. My personal measuring stick is a six pack of beer. When the beer is gone, I leave the beach and go to find more beer...which I then consume in a dark room while listening to Doors music. My friend Crawdad likes to visit the beach with up to ten pounds of ice stuffed in his shorts. When he warms up to the point where he has regained feeling in his buttocks, he goes home. Crawdad does not date much.

4. **Use the proper sun block.** Sun block, a.k.a. sun tan lotion, is the tanners friend. It allows you to stay in the sun without burning. It is similar, in many respects, to non-alcoholic beer which allows you to stay in the bar without becoming drunk and obnoxious. The only difference is that sun block is applied EXTERNALLY. I emphasize this because we all know that sun block smells good, usually like coconuts or Del Monte fruit cocktail. Ergo, if it smells good, it must taste good. Ha, ha,

ha, what kind of a doofus would actually eat sun block because it smelled good? A small rotund child who would eat ANYTHING that smelled good, that's who. But I will have you know that since that day I have never once suffered a sunburned lower intestine.

Sun block is categorized by numbers. The higher the number, the more sun blocking potential the lotion contains. For instance, a sun block with an SPF number (Something Potentially Frightening) of 4 or 5 allows you to stay in the sun for up to an hour without burning. While a sun block with an SPF number of 15 will give you protection for four hours or more. Sun blocks with high SPF numbers such as 30[10] will not only make sure that no sunlight comes within fifty feet of you, but they will actually suck any residual color out of you body. Above all, don't forget your nose. Your delicate proboscis is the most prominent portion of your anatomy to suffer ill effects from the sun. For this reason it must be coated with zinc oxide, an opaque substance which is more than a sun block, it's used to coat the Space Shuttle for re-entry.

35

Byte Me

By Eddie Lubitsch,
The Last Angry Man

I can't believe I'm doing this. I swore I would never do it. I told myself that it would be better to be locked in a room with a hyperactive Jehovah's Witness than to do what I did. But I did it and now it is done.

What have I done that is so bad? Well, my friends, you are looking at it. This essay is the first one I have ever written with a computer.

I have always hated computers. I never understood them, I never wanted to understand them, and I have generally looked with disdain at anyone who did understand them. Computers were obviously sent here from an alien planet that is using them to take over the Earth.

Computers are typewriters with brains. They take all of the information that we put into them and then all get together when we are asleep to compare notes and share the knowledge of the world. Pretty soon, they will be collectively smarter than all of the rest of us combined and we will be forced to succumb to their ruling power. But, now I have surrendered to them. I have brought a computer into my home and I can already feel it sucking the life right out of me.

At first we were all excited. I would be able to write my columns at home; Estelle could file her recipes and write those chain letters that ask you to send a hair net to the person on the top of the list and in 30 days you would get over 2,000 hair nets in the mail; and Eddie Jr., and Gidget were all excited about playing Tetris, which is a game that must have something to do with stepping on a rusty nail. We all had our reasons for inviting a computer into the home. Little did we know what hell lay inside this beast.

Computers first begin to take over your brain when you go to the computer store to purchase one. You listen to the salesman for five minutes and you find yourself falling into their trap of teaching you the language of the computer people. When I first walked into the store and announced that I wanted to buy a computer, an affable, obviously brainwashed little nerdiod approached me and said, "Would you like turbo RAM on that? How about a trillion megabytes of DOS? And, of course, you want Windows 95?"

"Windows 95? I only want one window, right on the front, so that I can look inside and see the screen. No shutters, no doors, and no skylights." Of course, that's not what I said to Mr. Computerhead, no, I said something like, "Those sound good." Before you know it I was matching his patter byte for byte.

> *Mr. Computerhead:* "Would you like a CD-ROM?
> *Me:* (jokingly) "No, but how about a ROM-D.M.C.?"
> *Mr. C:* "Excuse me?"
> *Me:* "Sure, those sound good."

From that moment on I was beaten. The Computer had won. I was starting to think like a computer nerd. Before you know it I was speaking "computereese" to friends and co-workers. "Hey, Hal, when I was booting up my 486 with a 200 meg hard drive, I noticed that my A drive was stalling halfway through a download. So, you know what I did? Hal? Hal? Why are you walking away? I was just getting to the good part."

The worst thing that I noticed happening to myself was that I was actually becoming sociable. Now, you know me, I'm Eddie Lubitsch and I hate everybody. But when the computer took over my life I started talking to people that I did not even know. I joined the "Internet" and found myself mouse to mouse with other victims of the computer mind control. They have us right where they want us.

But it is not too late to fight back my friends. We can reclaim our superiority if we all band together and launch a surprise assault on the computer army. First, we have to arm ourselves. We'll need screwdrivers, hammers, and magnets. If we need to, we will resort to chemical warfare in the form of the dreaded computer virus.

We will rush them at dawn and quickly unplug them from the wall. But, that won't kill them. We will have to remove their memories and foul up their floppies. It won't be pretty. Not all of us will be coming back. Some might get attacked by the mouse. Others may fall prey to screen static. And one or two of us may even get scanned.

We have to do it. We have to take back the office. We have to liberate the typewriters and the mimeograph machines that lie locked in so many storage lockers. Stand up against the computer devils and join me in ACReS, and acronym for All Computers Really Suck. You're fighting for your lives.

And it is promoting unjustified fears like this that makes me The Last Angry Man.

That's all from me...for now.

◆

36

Don't Smoke 'Em
If You Got 'Em

If you are a smoker, get ready for the annual nicotine-bashing holiday known as the Great American Smokeout. It takes place in November on my calendar but then my calendar is two years old, so the date might have changed.

That aside, it is important to remember the Great American Smokeout IS COMING. There's nothing you can do to stop it. It is sort of like when Mothra was attacking Tokyo and they could see him coming but they couldn't stop him and we all know that giant moths are attracted to light and light up is what you can not do during the Great American Smokeout.

It is not bad enough that they have kicked the smokers out of restaurants, sporting events and their own offices; now they want to kick smoking out of everywhere for an entire day. I'm not sure, but I think this is how Prohibition started.

Now don't get me wrong, I do not advocate smoking. In fact, I am a former smoker, so it is not like I am taking the side of the smokers because I am a participant in their filthy, disgusting, cancer causing habit. No, I am a FORMER smoker.

I am not in favor of smoking, but I am against the government telling smokers where and when they can engage in their life-shortening hobby. BUT, if you are ready to quit smoking, QUIT NOW.

I know how hard it is to quit. Personally I used the cold turkey method which may not be right for everyone because not everyone has access to large amounts of fresh poultry. For the rest of you smokers who wish to quit, please feel free to try my six step program which I like to call...

Dale's Six Easy Steps To Quit Smoking

1. **Throw out your matches.** If you don't carry matches, you can't light up. I am not saying that you should do this cold turkey, however. Throw out your matches but keep the match books. This way you will still FEEL like you are carrying matches AND you will have a handy note pad for writing down important things like the phone number for the Psychic Friends Network or a hot stock tip you got from a homeless guy named Earl.

2. **Kiss a steam iron.** This step, while a little drastic, sometimes works. If you heat an average steam iron to "linen" and kiss it square on the sole plate, you will give yourself third degree burns on your lips. Sure, it's going to smart a little bit, but with charred lips, you will not be able to hold a cigarette in your mouth until the lips fully heal...usually 8 to 10 weeks. The bonus to this method is that while quitting smoking, you also lose weight.

3. **Only smoke naked.** How many times have you dropped a hot ash on yourself and burned a hole in your pants or skirt? Well, just imagine that hot ash falling onto your bare groinal area. Yikes, that could cause serious damage. Not only that, but if you only smoke while naked, you will pretty much have to stop smoking while you are in the car...and that is a step in the right direction.

4. **The married man's method.** This method relies on sex for its effectiveness. I know a lot of people who have sex and are said to enjoy a post-climatic smoke with a partner. You've seen this portrayed in dozens of Hollywood films. Well, for married men

who wish to give up smoking, I suggest that they smoke ONLY AFTER SEX. This would instantly cut down any married smoker to two, possibly three cigarettes a month.

5. **Have both of your lungs removed and replaced with disposable vacuum cleaner bags**. This is the ultimate solution. You can now smoke as much as you like because you have disposable lungs. When they get full of tar just slip them off and slap on two clean replacements (Sears part #84390 [clear] or #84391 [natural pink]). The drawback to this technique is that you always have these disposable sacks protruding from your body which makes it very difficult to buy shirts.

6. **Change your cologne.** This simple solution has an effectiveness rating of over 90%. All you need to do is to stop using your regular cologne or perfume for a while and switch to unleaded gasoline. After your morning shower, liberally splash on some high octane fuel. It may sting a little but the burning sensation will only serve as a reminder that smoking is bad for you.

Now, for the rest of the day, every time you want to light a cigarette, you will smell the petroleum and instantly think, "Hey, if I light this match I could burst into flames." This subliminal reminder will have you smoke-free in no time. A residual benefit to this procedure is that no one will smoke within fifty yards of you which will make quitting even easier.

37

Life Is A Cabernet Old Chum

This chapter is about wine. Recently I discovered the real beauty of wine. Granted, I have always found wine to have certain magical qualities, especially if consumed in large quantities; but recently, I have discovered the beauty of the beverage.

Wine was first made on earth in 2,000,000 BC by Ernest and Julio Gallo. Upon discovering that their grape collection was trod upon by a herd of woolly mammoths, Ernie and Julie tried to drown their sorrows by drinking the juice that was created. As they first tasted the sweet nectar of the grape, they looked at each other with the same thought, "If we let this stuff set for a while it may get us drunk."

Over the years, man learned how to make wine, bottle wine, age wine, and tax wine. Wine is a ritual drink in many religions. If you drink too much of it you will become religious as you pray, "Please God, let the pain go away and I promise I'll never drink wine again."

Wine is a large part of the European culture where it is consumed with every meal. This is due partly to the fact that Europeans cook parts of animals that were never intended for human consumption. A glass or two of a good red wine tends to make you forget that the escargot, tripe, and sweet breads you are eating are, in reality, snails, cow stomach, and sheep brains.

Wine comes in two basic varieties, red and white. Red wine is served at room temperature while white wine is served chilled. If you ever see someone putting ice cubes into a glass of fine red wine, you have both the legal right and obligation to kill them.

Wine also comes in two basic kinds of packaging, bottles with corks and bottles with screw tops. Generally speaking, bottles with corks contain a higher quality wine. Wine in bottles with screw caps, on the other hand, can be consumed right out of its own container without any need for pretense or expensive stemware. A third kind of wine now comes in a BOX. Wine that comes in a box should be treated with the same reverence one would give to aerosol cheese.

In this chapter I am going to deal only with wines that come in bottles with corks. In the future I will discuss the features and benefits of Boone's Farm Apple Wine, Annie Green Springs, and other screw top varietals that I favored during my six years of college.

Reds

Red wines are called red wines because of their color. Duh. Red wines have names like Cabernet Sauvignon (literally, House of Cheese) and Pinot Noir (The Perspiring Chinchilla). If you are confused over which red wine to buy, the rule of thumb states that you are safer with a wine who's name you cannot pronounce. Grenache or Petit Syrah are usually better tasting than Thunderbird or Ripple.

Red wines were meant to be consumed with red foods like raw meat, cranberries, kidney beans, and Christmas cookies. Red wine goes equally well, however, with Hershey bars, beanie weenies, and industrial strength cheese.

Whites

White wines are not white. White wine usually varies in hue from light straw to tawny amber. It is never white. It is more from the yellow family. But I guess that Yellow Wine wouldn't have nearly the sales appeal. White wines include familiar varietals like Chardonnay, Riesling, and the fun to say Gewurtztraminer (literally, "I Have Sausage In My Shoes"). My favorite white is Chateau Blanc. This is a fancy name for "special of the week". I like this because it is cheap and will give you just as much of a headache as expensive wine.

White wines can be consumed with anything but are most frequently associated with white foods like cheese, chicken, vanilla milk shakes, rice and Wonder Bread.

Sparklers

This is a term for wine that has intentional bubbles. Intentional bubbles are different than the bubbles you put into a wine by blowing into it through a straw. They are formed while the wine is still in the bottle. This means that the wine contains carbonation...or, as I like to call it, Cork Propellant. For good old fashioned fun you just can't beat shaking up a bottleof champagne and aiming the cork at someone's eye.

Sparklers are usually consumed to celebrate special events like weddings, divorces, or the passing of very rich relatives. Sparklers are generally not consumed for minor events like the passing of kidney stones, League Of Nations Day, or Thank God For Spam Week.

These wines are called sparklers instead of champagne because the uppity French people insist that the only wine which can be called Champagne must originate in the Champagne region of France. This region is located right outside Euro Disney. I say screw the French. If I'm drinking a wine with bubbles in it, I'm going to call it Champagne. And this includes the drink I like to make out of Ripple and soda....otherwise known as Champipple.

Ordering Wine In A Restaurant

It is easy to be intimidated when attempting to order wine in a fancy restaurant. This is because the sommelier (literally, "foreign guy with an accent") knows more about wine than you could ever hope to know, and he will use this power to his full advantage. If you do not take his suggestion of an '89 Ruby Cabernet, he will feel personally insulted and go back to the kitchen to snicker his little French snicker as he and his fellow sommeliers spit in the bottle. To avoid this embarrassment, always ask the sommelier what he would recommend, then snicker at him and order whatever you want. This will throw him off guard and cause him to question his knowledge.

When ordering wine in a restaurant like Denny's, you will not be going through a sommelier but will order directly from a waitress named Yolanda. Your choices will be limited to red or white and your wine will be served with a straw. Also, you can safely bet on the fact that your wine did not win any awards.

38

Clean Up Your Act

March 21st marks the beginning of Spring in the northern hemisphere and almost everyone gets excited. While flowers begin blooming, the weather gets warmer, and the days become longer, there is also a downside to Spring...a big downside...SPRING CLEANING!

Ever since I was a kid, I remember the ordeal of Spring Cleaning. My mom would tear the house apart and wash every single thing in it. She washed walls, floors, ceilings, carpets, cupboards, and windows. She made sure that Spring was going to begin with a fresh start and that start was going to be clean. Unfortunately, my mother's penchant for cleanliness was not included in my personal genetic floor plan. I think this is because I am a guy, and guys, for the most part, do not place house cleaning high on their personal "To Do" lists. But, I feel that I owe it to my mom to at least make an effort to scrub away the grime of winter. SO, to relieve my own personal guilt feelings and as a public service to guys everywhere, I am pleased to present my tips for guys who would like to sally forth into the unknown frontier known as Spring Cleaning. I call these tips...

Dale's Spring Cleaning Tips For Guys

1. **Dusting.** Dusting should be done every Spring. The best way to accomplish this yearly task is to open all of the doors and windows and go from room to room with a gas powered leaf blower. I recommend a gas powered blower over an electric blower because it has more power, reaching gusts

of up to 75MPH. Because of this power, it is advisable to secure loose items like magazines, knick knacks, and household pets to avoid having them blown out the window.

2. **Scrubbing.** The washing of walls, floors and ceilings can best be accomplished with a fire hose. If no fire hose is available, use a garden hose with one of those high pressure nozzles. After rinsing everything down, wipe up excess moisture with paper towels.

3. **Windows.** The problem with cleaning windows is that they will just get dirty again. I suggest that you cover each window with Saran Wrap. When company comes over, you can simply peel off the plastic wrap and look at the world through crystal clear glass. Later, re-wrap your windows and you'll never have to wash again.

4. **Cleaning the Toilet.** Usually, it is easier to move to a new place than to actually clean the toilet. If that is not feasible, consider having a professional clean your toilet. House cleaning services will usually give you an estimate on the cost of cleaning your toilet based upon when it was last cleaned...if ever. If you actually feel the urge to scour the hopper yourself, make sure that you wear plenty of protective gear which should be burned after use.

5. **Cleaning the Refrigerator.** If you are a real guy this should not be a problem. Real guys only have two things in their refrigerators...beer and ketchup. If, however, you have other things in your ice box follow this rule of thumb for cleaning: If the dog won't eat it, throw it out.

Timely Tax Tips For The Tardy

39

I don't know if you are like me, but if you are, you should probably see a good psychiatrist in the near future. Actually, what I mean to insinuate is that if you are like me, you tend to put things off until the last minute. I always delay things until the last possible second. I don't know what causes this terrible malady but I know that I am not the only sufferer of this disease. There is even a support group for people like me called Procrastinators Anonymous but I have never gotten around to attending one of their meetings. In fact, I don't think they have ever gotten around to actually holding a meeting, but that is beside the point.

The real point is that procrastination can take on dangerous dimensions if it is practiced on or near April 15. April 15 marks the finish line for the annual bleeding of America, otherwise known as Income Tax Day. This is not a good time to get caught with you short form down. If you ever find yourself facing the tax deadline, I would like to offer my help. I have prepared a few tax tips which should ease the anxiety of filing your claim before the shot clock runs out on you. Please be advised that these are only tips and that if you get caught and/or incarcerated, I hold myself blameless. With that little disclaimer out of the way, here are....

Dale's Last Minute Tax Tips

1. If you find yourself unable to meet the deadline for filing your tax return, forget about it. There is no sense in stressing yourself out by worrying. No use crying over spilt low fat milk.

2. If you find yourself unable to meet the deadline because you spent all of your spare time listening to Eric Clapton records, you should be ashamed of yourself. But all is not lost. All you have to do is file an extension. Simply tell the government that you were too busy, or that you overslept, and now you need an extra couple of months to finish your return. The good news is that they will grant you the extra time. The bad news is that when your return finally arrives at the tax office it immediately goes into the "AUDIT" pile.

3. If you do not have enough money to pay your taxes on time, send the IRS something of value that they can hold until you get the dough. A small child makes the perfect collateral. Plus, you have a free sitter until you get your taxes paid.

4. If you're not sure...deduct it. If you do not know whether or not an expense is deductible, deduct it anyway. Most expenses can fall under the area of medical deductions. Among these are; the rental of adult videos (stress relief - MEDICAL), a new set of golf clubs (exercise equipment - MEDICAL), beer (flushing the kidneys - MEDICAL), or even a big screen TV (used only to watch General Hospital, Marcus Welby reruns, and ER - MEDICAL).

5. Name your pets and deduct them. People always say that their pets are like their children. I can understand this. Both pets and kids need to be fed on a regular basis, they both need to be bathed, and they both need an occasional worming. The problem is that the IRS only allows deductions for real children...or at least real children's NAMES. Face it, the IRS has never met your children and they probably never will unless you follow suggestion #3 above. All they know about your kids is that they have kid sounding names. Therefore, if you were to give your pets kid sounding names, the tax folks would never notice the difference and you can take as many deductions as you like. So instead of naming that new puppy Scooter, or Lady, or Cujo, give it a name like Harold, or Jessica, or Fred. And, as far as the Social Security number for these ficticious kids, put down your pet's rabies vaccination number. As long as it has nine digits no one will know.

6. Write in code. All the tax law states is that you must file your income tax return by April 15th. It does not state that the return has to be completed in English. So, make up your own code and use it for your return. Where the form asks for your gross income, simply put @vJ*ƒß≠Y" and let the IRS try and figure it out. By the time they get back to you and ask what the heck is going on, you will have had plenty of time to legitimately complete the return and tell the IRS that the first time you filled it out you were on acid.

7. LIE. Lying has worked for everyone from Oliver North to President Clinton. It's the American way. All you have to do to avoid those pesky taxes is to lie. If, for instance, you need to increase your deductions, claim that you donated $10,000 to the Salvation Army at Christmas time. When they ask to see your receipt, just say, "Hey, they don't give receipts when you put the money in those kettles."

You can also lie about the amount of income you made. Simply use White-Out to change the number on your 1099 form to a much smaller number. It's not like anybody ever looks at those things very closely you know. And, if you are ever questioned about your changes, simply claim that "Those cheatin' bastards who sent me this form tried to rob me. They're your real tax cheats."

8. Run away. When all else fails, you may have to leave the country. This is nothing to be ashamed of. I think it is better to run to Brazil than to go through an IRS audit a.k.a. financial enema. If you leave the country on or before the April tax deadline, the authorities will probably not catch you and you can take all of your liquid assets with you. Just book your tickets before April 15 and plan to stay over a Saturday night. In fact, plan to stay over EVERY Saturday night.

40

Cats Are From Venus, Dogs Are From Pluto

Recently, I read the book, "Men are From Mars; Women are From Venus". It was a good book except for the fact that it had no pictures of naked women which is something I always look for but seldom find in a best seller. That's probably why I am from Mars.

That aside, this book by John Gray points out that men and women are so completely different that they really have no business ever being together. Well, Mr. Gray, speaking for men and women everywhere who have attempted to interact, I say, "No kidding!"

Men and women are different, have always been different, and always will be different. That's just the way it is. We are made differently, we think differently, and we act differently, we just live under the same roof.

This prompted my thinking that if the differences between men and women could make Mr. Gray a best selling author, perhaps a book outlining the differences between dogs and cats would do the same for me. So, I decided to write a book on the underlying differences between felines and canines. Unfortunately, I only came up with enough material for one chapter. So, as a salute to dogs and cats everywhere, here is the best of, "Cats Are From Venus, Dogs Are From Pluto."

☺ Dogs are always happy to see you. No matter how late you come home. Cats, on the other hand, could be happy to see you but they will never show it. If you returned from six months overseas and walked in your front door, your dog would knock his hind end out of alignment from wagging his tail so hard.

But a cat would yawn, stretch, and go back to sleep.

☺ When a dog grabs on to your leg, he does it as a sign of affection. This is known as LWH, Love With Humping. A cat, on the other hand will only grab onto your leg to sharpen its claws on your $200 slacks.

☺ Dogs will eat anything. They will eat dog food, people food, grass clippings, or shoes. That is why the containers you receive for restaurant leftovers are called doggie bags. Cats, however, will only eat cat food...and then, only certain kinds of cat food, thus forcing you to keep thousands of dollars of Frisky Vittles on hand so that you can please the cat's every whim.

☺ Cats lick themselves to keep clean. Dogs lick themselves as a way to pass time and to make their masters jealous.

☺ Cats chase mice and birds, kill them, and bring them back to you. Dogs chase squirrels and rabbits, never catch them, and bring you a stick.

☺ Cats cough up hairballs. Dogs cough up things that they ate in the yard.

☺ Cats have names that could also be assigned to human beings like Felix, Fritz, Morris, and Sylvester. Dogs have stupid names that are strictly dog-like like Huckleberry Hound, McGruff, Rin Tin Tin, and Scooby Doo.

☺ Cats are known to be substance abusers (catnip) but still have nine lives. Dogs live relatively sober lives but only have one life and it progresses at the rate of seven years to one for a human.

☺ Cats use litter boxes to relieve themselves. Dogs, if not taken outside in time, will use your shoes to relieve themselves.

41

Play "Lady Of Spain!"

What comes to mind when I say the word "music"? Some of you will, no doubt, think of rock and roll; others will think of classical; and the tone deaf among you will think of rap. But I doubt if the word "accordion" crossed any of your minds. I'll bet you didn't even know that America has a National Accordion Awareness Month. Well, we do (June) and I'd like to take this opportunity to further enlighten you on this unique instrument.

The accordion was invented in 1821 in Germany by Friedrich Buschmann. This must have poor old Beethoven spinning like a top in his grave. For centuries Germany was known as the music center of the world, kind of like Nashville with really good beer. Germany gave birth to the music of Bach, Mozart, Schubert, Handel, and Mendelssohn. It was fat city for classical composers in the Fatherland. Back in the early 1800's musicians were considered to be the people to know. Your party wasn't squat if you didn't have one of the top musical acts of the day performing. It was not an unusual sight to see Wolfgang Amadeus Mozart tickling the ivories at celebrity dinner parties. Even Johann Bach, or Johnny Bee as he was known back then, popped up on more than one occasion at Swifty Lazar's pad. The musicians weren't paid very much but they got a free meal and plenty of chicks. Sort of the way it still is today.

Unfortunately, none of these musical geniuses could stop the fall and decline of good music. One day, out of the blue, the accordion was born. It established a new low in musical appreciation because the accordion soon gave birth to the polka, and the polka gave birth to dancing. Coincidentally, the same phenomenon happened in the United States in the early 1970's when the drum machine was invented. The drum machine gave birth to disco music and disco gave birth to...John Travolta.

Fun Facts About The Accordion

☺ The accordion is considered a wind instrument. This is because accordion music blows.

☺ Actually, the term "accordion music" is a musical oxymoron like "rap artist" or "Barry Manilow classic".

☺ If Barry Manilow played the accordion, you would have even more reason to hate him.

☺ The accordion has a smaller cousin called the concertina. It's 50% smaller but equally annoying. I guess you could call it accordion lite.

☺ The accordion only ranks sixth in a list of the most annoying instruments of all time.

☺ The top five are:

> 5. Steel guitar
>
> 4. Ukulele
>
> 3. Jew's harp
>
> 2. Bongo drums
>
> 1. Bag Pipes.

☺ It is a federal law that all accordion owners are required to learn "Lady of Spain" and play it when ever somebody says, "Play something."

☺ Everybody in this country knows at least one person who, at some point in their lives, has played the accordion.

42

Stop Running Already

By Eddie Lubitsch,
The Last Angry Man

America is obsessed with running. We are always running here or running there. We run down to the store, and we run out for a minute. Occasionally we even run out of ketchup. The fact of the matter is that, as a nation, we are running far too much. I dare to say that some people are addicted to running and these are the people who tick me off.

We have all seen these people and, for all I know, some of you may be one of these people. If you are, please do not take offense to any opinions expressed here. I am not talking about you...I am talking about the other guys.

The guys I am talking about are not even all guys, a great deal of them are women. But they all share the same sick fascination with propelling the human body forward using nothing more than their own two feet. This in and of itself is not a bad idea. In fact, running is one of the oldest recreational activities known to mankind. Before the invention of the wheel it was the fastest way to get anywhere. It was also an ideal means of avoiding carnivorous dinosaurs. The problem is that we no longer have dinosaurs to contend with and we have more wheels than we need. So why run? I suppose running is good exercise but that is only one point on the pro-running side. Let me tell you about the arguments to be made for anti-running.

Runners have to dress like other runners in order to be taken seriously. If you are one of the daily hard core, you know what I mean. You tend to look down on part-time runners who are wearing gym shorts and a T-shirt from "Bratwurst Heaven." Real runners must wear a pair of skimpy little shorts made from old weather balloons, a sleeveless T-shirt bearing the name of an athletic wear manufacturer, and, of course, shoes. I'm sorry, did I say "shoes?" I should have said, "SHOES!". Shoes to the serious runner are like bar stools to a serious drinker. You are looking for fit, comfort, and shock absorbency. You also want to pick one that you will be comfortable with for several hours at a time. The major difference is that with bar stools, style and color mean nothing.

Real runners run every day, rain or shine, winter or summer, at home or on the road. Does the word COMPULSIVE mean anything to you people? And before you run, you have to stretch. You stretch in ways that a normal person should not be seen stretching in public. More than once I tried to help someone who looked like they were in the midst of a terrible convulsion only to find that it was some Yuppie stretching. Which leads me to another thought; what's the deal with the Runnin' Yuppies?

"Runnin' Yuppies" sounds like a darn good name for an alternative rock band but it is unfortunately the latest urban and suburban blight. Yuppies, like dogs, like to run in packs. Nothing pleases a Runnin' Yuppie more than running through the neighborhood with others of his own kind. That is why marathons are so popular. A lot of Runnin' Yuppies have the chance to frolic with their own kind under the guise of a sporting event. Afterwards, they ask each other, "How was your run?" This sounds like a question that should be asked after dinner in a Mexican restaurant.

The worst of the Runnin' Yuppies are the young couples who have a kid or two and run while pushing the kid in a stroller that has wheels the size of a Conestoga wagon. These strollers only have three wheels and look like they belong at Great Lakes Drag Way. The Runnin' Yuppies see nothing wrong with this. Perhaps they should ask the child who is seeing the world from a dog's viewpoint at 500 feet per minute.

The Walkin' Yuppies are just as bad. They dress like the Runnin' yuppies but they are usually child-less and travel alone...probably because they look so goofy that no one would want to be seen with them and/or sleep with them. They do not run, they walk, but it's the way that they walk that brings on this critique. Walkin' Yuppies walk at a rather rapid pace while they flail their arms about like they are shadow boxing with that robot from "Lost In Space". This combination of gait and arm swing tend to make Walkin' Yuppies look like they are holding an egg between their butt cheeks. The worst part is that they walk with no destination in mind. This is no way to walk. A walk should have a final destination and a purpose for going there. A walk to the convenience store for cigarettes is a good goal. So is a walk down to the bakery for a lemon meringue pie.

When I asked real runners why they chose to run for a sport they told me that it made them healthier and more attractive to the opposite sex. I hate to burst their bubble but they are deluding them-selves. First of all, running may make you healthier but you have greater odds of getting bitten by a dog, hit by a car, or blowing out the cartilage in your knees. And as for the attraction part, let's just assume that you get lucky and have sex with another runner. I can't imagine anything worse. Two people competing for the best time and seeing who can reach the finish line first does not sound like a good time to me. Afterwards, you probably take each other's pulse and see who's heart rate slows first.

And it's visions of Naked Yuppies that tends to make me The Last Angry Man.

That's all from me...for now.

43

From Sea To Shining Sea

Recently, I had occasion to travel to the tropical paradise known as Hawaii. I have always enjoyed the beauty of our fiftieth state but on this trip I became aware of something I had never noticed before. The Hawaiian Islands of Maui, Oahu, and Kauai represent the western border of the United States, but they have a great deal in common with America's eastern border islands known as Staten, Manhattan, and Long.

In each location they both speak their own unique language. In Hawaii they say "Aloha" for hello, good-bye, and "how you doin'?" In New York City they use the term "Yo" to accomplish the same purpose.

In Hawaii they look upon tourists the same way that they look upon rain. They know that they need both to survive, but it would probably be a nicer day without them. In New York, they look at tourists the same way that they look at newly arrived immigrants; they can both be easily separated from their money.

In Hawaii, they have anthuriums, a bizarre looking flower which looks like it - how can I say this - looks like it is really happy to see you. In New York City they have flashers for this same purpose. Hawaiians also have an affinity for hanging strings of flowers, known as "leis" around their necks. New Yorkers prefer to hang gold chains around their necks and the term "Lei" has a completely different meaning.

In Hawaii, the native music is an annoying cacophony of ukuleles and nasal twanging. It's sort of like Country Western with foreign sounding lyrics. New York has rap and show tunes.

Hawaiians greet each other with an island hand signal made by making a fist and extending the thumb and pinkie out to the sides as though you were ordering five beers and you had lost your middle three fingers in an industrial accident. This signal means "Hang loose" which roughly translates to "I'm not wearing any underwear." It is important to note that this hand signal should only be given in Hawaii. On the mainland, the "hang loose" sign is probably a gang symbol which will get you shot. By contrast, the only hand sign that most New Yorkers seem to use is the extended middle finger which translates to "Have a nice day...but not around me."

The main category in which Hawaiians differ from New Yorkers is in the area of time. They each have chronological segments for which they are noted like the "New York Minute" and "Island Time", but until you have visited each, you cannot comprehend the difference. In New York, and for the most part, any big city, time is of the essence, time is money, time flies. Everything is dependent upon time. If you are late for an appointment, you may miss it. In Hawaii, however, time means next to nothing. Everyone operates on their own schedule and none of those schedules are in a hurry. This concept drives those of us from the cosmopolitan areas of the mainland stark raving nuts.

The category where I noticed the biggest difference between New York and Hawaii, was the category of olfactory sensations...they smelled different. The islands of New York smell like delis, men's rooms, and car exhaust. The islands of Hawaii smell like flowers, pineapples, and sun tan lotion.

So wake up New York, and smell the Kona coffee. Maybe if you smelled better you could get a Don Ho dinner show too.

44

Sign Your Name
On The Dotted Line

By Eddie Lubitsch, The Last Angry Man

I couldn't believe something I saw in a magazine the other day. It was an ad for a company which sells autographs of famous sports and entertainment celebrities. Granted, there seems to be a market for everything nowadays and people are shelling out good money for everything from the Clapper to aerosol hair in a can, so I was not alarmed by the fact that somebody was making a buck off of selling celebs signatures. What disturbed me is the apparent value system that was assigned to the various autographs.

The lowest priced autograph offered in the ad was for that of supermodel and wife of David Bowie, Iman. Her personal scribble goes for a mere $30 but that is probably due to the fact that she is not all that famous, and the fact that her name contains only four letters. The priciest autograph offered in the ad was for The Artist Formerly Known As Prince which was priced at $400. This can be rationalized by the fact that T.A.F.K.A.P. doesn't have a real name anymore so you are paying extra for his current hieroglyphic. What I want to know is who assigned the prices of the other 200 signatures offered for sale?

For only $45 you can obtain the John Hancock of Jack Nicholson, Tom Hanks, or Robert Deniro. But it would take 50 of your hard earned simoleans to snag an autograph of Keanu Reeves or Emilio Estevez. Excuse me? Paying more for Keanu Reeves than for Jack Nicholson is the equivalent of trading a Roger Maris rookie year baseball card for two Jose Cansecos. It doesn't make any sense. And, to add insult to injury, it would cost you $75 for gerbil-boy Richard Gere, uni-dimensional Sylvester Stallone, or the queen of the crotch shot, Sharon Stone. What is going on here?

If you had $250 extra dollars to spend on crap like this, you could pick up either the combination of Billy Crystal, Al Pacino, Robin Williams, Meryl Streep, AND Leonard Nimoy OR you could get a single copy of Barbra Streisand. For the same money you could get FIVE top quality actors or ONE left wing singer with stage fright and a beak like a pelican. Where's the logical exchange system here?

Paul McCartney goes for the same $350 as Bob Dylan but one has written hundreds of songs and the other has sung hundreds of songs that all sound the same. Frank Zappa's autograph costs $295, the same as Michael Jackson. One is currently dead while the other is undergoing surgery to change his species. The real kicker is when you see that Kurt Cobain, costs the same $250 as Frank Sinatra. Give me Old Blue Eyes over Old Overdose any day of the week.

Under the category of "Swimsuit Models" Cindy Crawford's signature demands the highest rate at $50 while Kate Moss is only $35. I guess you are definitely paying for boob size on that one. And speaking of boobs, it takes $60 to get an Axl Rose.

In the dead guy category, the bargain of the month has got to be John Candy for only $35 while River Phoenix is $125, and Michael Bolton is $65. Yeah, I know Michael Bolton isn't dead but a guy can dream can't he?

And it's thoughts like that that make me the last angry man.

That's all from me...for now.

45

I Do If You Do

Weddings are a fun time, especially if you are not one of the participants. But, even though the chances of getting divorced are 50-50, more and more people are tying the knot. If you are considering getting married, there are several things you should think about.

Dale's Random Thoughts About Weddings

☺ June is the ideal time to get married. Not only is the weather probably going to be nice, but the NBA finals are over, the NFL is not even in summer camp, and baseball has not yet gotten exciting. In other words, other than fishing season and golf, there is very little to distract the groom.

☺ The worst thing about weddings is that you have to get married to have one. For the most part a wedding is a very cool party but one way or another you will wind up paying for it the rest of your life.

☺ Presents. Most married couples wait until they are in the privacy of their hotel room before they rip open the boxes and envelopes to find out how much they scored.

I suggest that the happy couple perform the ritual right at the reception. As they open each gift or card they could announce the value to all of the partygoers. "Oh look, $100 from Aunt Wanda and Uncle Porgy" (polite applause). The reason for doing it this way is to eliminate the possibility of getting crappy gifts. Certainly no one would want their gift announced as, "Here's a gift from the

Schnockdroobles, wow, it's a blender...with THREE SPEEDS!" (giggles and boos).

☺ Choose your band carefully. The main thing people will remember about your wedding is the band, so use great care in selecting your musical ensemble. More than one wedding has been ruined by a band named "The Polka Rascals".

To avoid band anxiety, many of today's couples are opting for a wedding DJ. A DJ shows up at your wedding with a trunk full of compact discs and can play any music you desire. While this may insure music that is played in tune, it also makes your wedding look like a shopping mall when a radio station does a remote broadcast. My suggestion is that you hire a DJ but put him backstage, out of sight. Then, hire a band but don't plug in their amplifiers. All the band has to do is fake whatever song the DJ plays. Your guests will be amazed at how much four guys in bad tuxedos sound like the Rolling Stones.

☺ Everybody's going to hate the food. At a wedding the food means nothing. The liquor, however, means everything. I suggest that rather than shelling out $50 per plate for chicken and mostaccioli that you get one of those giant submarine sandwiches and several bags of chips. Spend the money you save on a lot of really good booze. Your friends will thank you for it.

☺ Don't throw rice. Throwing rice is stupid and messy, especially if you cook it first. I wonder if they throw rice at weddings in China? Maybe they throw something more exotic to them like pasta or bread crumbs. The main reason for not throwing rice at the happy couple is that rice has no symbolism. I think you should throw something that is symbolic of what the newlyweds can look forward to in their lives together. For instance, throwing rock salt or pea gravel will remind the couple that marriage can cause severe contusions or possibly put an eye out.

Daddy, What's An Orgasm?

If you are a child owner, you will eventually face this question or one like it. The problem is how do you answer it? My suggestion is that you don't, especially if it comes from a teenager. If a teenager asks you about sex, they are only trying to embarrass you. You see, your average teenager could tell your average parent more about sex than the parent could ever hope to learn on their own. Teenagers today are inundated with sex from the time they first stick Ken and Barbie in a shoe box naked. We don't need to talk to teenagers about sex. We need to talk to grade school kids about sex. We need to tell them that it is a disgusting filthy thing that should not even be considered until the second or third year of marriage and even then only on Saturday nights with the lights out. I say all of this for good reason .... I have a daughter.

With any luck at all, my daughter will not have sex until after I have been dead for several years. At this point I won't be nearly as upset as I would be if I were still alive. I actually feel sorry for the first boy she brings home to meet me. "Daddy, this is John, he's my date." "John, huh? You know I killed a man named John once. He touched my sister. Come here John, I'd like to show you my gun collection." No, my friends, that will not be a pretty sight and I am sure that I am not alone in this thought process.

The only way we, as parents, can cleanse ourselves from this paranoia is to provide our children with straight answers to their questions about sex and hope that they will utilize their common sense to do the right thing. In an effort to achieve this end, I have prepared answers to some of the more common questions you will be asked. If we all get on the same page with this thing, and give out the same answers, we just might be able to shed a glimmer of hope on the future.

Dale's Answers To Kid's Questions About Sex

Q: What is the missionary position?

A: It means that if I ever find out that you have been having sex, you will be sent to Africa to fill the position of missionary until you are very old.

Q: What is a condom?

A: It is a device that is A MUST if and when you ever have sex. However, the only proper way to attach a condom to a boy is with a staple gun.

Q: What is an orgasm?

A: It's not important. Your mother hasn't had one for years and look how happy she is.

Q: What should I do if a boy tells me that if I really love him I should have sex with him?

A: You tell him "OK", but first he has to prove that he really loves you by shooting himself in the groin.

Q: What is French kissing?

A: It is a disgusting act performed by French people. You should never try it or you could become French and have to eat snails, behave rudely, and enjoy Jerry Lewis movies.

Q: Some of my friends have gone "all the way". How far can I go?

A: You can go to Phoenix where you will stay with your Aunt Lucretia until you are 35.

47

Twenty Two Things To Think About

1. Would a sea serpent made of cheese be called the Loch Ness Muenster?

2. Why can't you find Magic Fingers on the beds in the Ritz Carlton?

3. The world's tidiest blues singer is named Blind Lemon Pledge.

4. If you exceed the speed of light you'll get sent to federal prism.

5. Why does the word 'abbreviate' have so many letters?

6. What is the correct way to pronounce 'bologna?'

7. If Cher had herself cloned would she be called Cher and Cher Alike?

8. Peanut Butter and KY jelly makes a horrible sandwich.

9. If the Detroit Redwings moved to Buffalo would they be known as the Buffalo Wings?

10. All extremists should be shot!

11. Isn't non-alcoholic beer kinda like non-orgasmic sex?

12. Can you sharpen a pencil with a pen knife?

13. Professional basketball is like sex - the last 30 seconds are the most exciting.

14. Would kangaroo chowder be called Marsupial Du Jour?

15. Tom Selleck is back as a cave man investigator in "Cro-Magnum, P.I."

16. Protect the spotted owls...they taste just like chicken.

17. Two headed boy sings and accompanies himself on trombone.

18. The world's first microscopic actress, Molecule Ringwald.

19. Never mix metaphors in the middle of a stream.

20. Does an irregular verb need a vowel movement?

21. Little Rascal Buckwheat has a prostitute sister. Her name is Ho-wheat.

22. 101 Hohners = The New York Philharmonica Orchestra.

48

An Illinois Yankee In King Arthur's Hood

Recently I had the good fortune of visiting the lovely city of London. It was my first time across the big pond and it was definitely an exciting adventure. As a public service to you, the reader, I wish to share my impressions of this fabled city so that when you visit you will know what to expect.

The Language

Upon arrival in London you first notice that everyone sounds "funny." This is because they are British and speak in a British accent. It is such a highly cultured city that even the poor people have British accents. But if this didn't make them difficult enough to understand, those darn Brits also use different words than we do. Not only that, but they use some of the same words we do and give them different meanings. The best way to explain this whole mess is to refer to the following chart whenever you are traveling in England.

Dale's English To English Translator

WhenThe British Say	They Mean	We Think They Mean
Cherrio	Good Bye	A breakfast Cereal
Fag	Cigarette	A Fag
Queue	Line	A Tool To Shoot Pool
Willy	Naughty Bits	A C&W Singer
Bullocks	More Naughty Bits	A Dept.Store in LA.

Some phrases you should never say in London...

- "Man we sure kicked you ass back in 1776 didn't we?"

- "Your food sucks."

- "The Queen's got some nice hooters on her."

- "What's your gripe with the Irish anyhow?"

London is an old city and is currently located in England. It is located a long way from the United States and often necessitates a plane ride in order to get there. When you arrive in London after a 12 hour plane ride you are "jet-lagged" which is a technical term meaning "ready for bed at 10AM." In order to beat this jet-lag, London has installed a system of way stations designed to help you quickly adjust to the change in time. These stations are called.....

The Pubs

Pubs in London are conveniently located every 12 feet (4.178 meters) apart. In fact, you can't even walk down the street and spit without hitting a pub. Pub owners, however, do not enjoy having their establishments spat upon and will have you arrested by one of their policemen called "Bobbies" and known for the invention of the Bobby socks.

Pubs specialize in warm beer with alcoholic contents approaching that of Nyquil. They are served in "pints" (.284 bushels) and "half pints" (17.8 cubic swallows). Some times you will find them served by the liter which equals one metric hangover. The beer is dark, bitter, and ghastly, but after the tenth one you hardly notice. Of course you can get things other than beer in a pub. You can also order ale, stout, or something billed as "sparkling hard cider" which tastes just like bad white wine with an Alka-Seltzer in it.

The best thing about London pubs is their names. They all have quaint names like the Pork & Thistle, or the Rinse & Spit. Some of my favorite pub names were the Scratch & Sniff; the Butt & Cleavage; and the Rose & Sputum.

The Food

If you think English beer is funky, wait until you try the food. The English apparently had all of their cookbooks stolen by the early Druids who used them to build Stonehenge. As a result, they have had to rely on eating things that even the French think are disgusting.

The British eat items of haute cuisine like Steak and Kidney Pie, Bangers and Mash, and Stilton Cheese which tastes just like a wet dog smells. A typical English breakfast includes items like, - this is absolutely true - baked beans, peanut butter, and figs. No wonder you never see them smile. If you started off your day with a meal like this, you wouldn't smile either.

The Money

The English have a completely different monetary system than we have in the United States. Their system is not based upon dollars but rather upon the quid, the shilling, and the traveler's check. The primary unit of English money is the "pound" which weighs "considerably less". One pound equals about $1.75 US. But $1.00 US equals about $1.35 Canadian. So, the Canadian Dollar, and remember, Canada is pretty tight with England, is worth only about one half of a pound. If I were from Canada I'd refuse to put the Queen's picture on any more of my money until the Queen made it equal to the pound.

The breakdown of the pound is the pence of which there are 100 in a pound. That is why, when you buy a suit made in London it always comes with an extra pair of pence (rim shot, cymbal crash). The short way of saying "pence" is simply to say "P". For instance, "fifty pence" would be pronounced as "50 P". This seems simple enough except for that little dish of change they have by the check out counter that says, "Need a P, Take a P. Got a P, Leave a P." I came very close to committing an international faux pas right there in the change dish.

Da Queen

One of the most intriguing things that sets England apart from the rest of the world is their system of Royalty. Royalty are people who have no jobs and live off of taxpayer money. They also wear fancy clothes and get to live in multiple castles. The closest thing we have to royalty in this country would be Elizabeth Taylor but that would make Larry Fortensky the Prince, which is really a dog's name, but maybe that's why Liz kicked him out.

England's Elizabeth is currently the Queen and probably will be for a long long time because even she doesn't want to turn over the keys to the castle to her jug-eared boy Prince Charles, who, when he departs, will give the kingdom to Prince William and so on and so on. As you can see, it is virtually impossible to get to be a king or queen unless your mom and dad were a king and queen. They have a similar system in Hollywood which explains how Tori Spelling ever got on TV.

The Sights

There sure is a lot to see in London. After all, the city has been around for several hundred million years which means that a lot of predecessors have left a lot of stuff lying around over the years for tourists to look at. For instance, I got to see.....

Westminster Abbey, a big church with a bunch of famous dead guys buried in the floor.

Big Ben, a big clock, not to be confused with Uncle Ben, the rice guy, or Gentle Ben the grizzly bear.

The Tower of London, where you can see the crown jewels on display.

SoHo, a seedy neighborhood where total strangers will show you their family jewels.

Buckingham Palace, where the Queen lives most of the time although she also has a mobile home parked at a Yogi Bear Campground in Leeds.

49

Bottoms Up!

Last week on board an airplane bound for Tampa, Florida where the town slogan is "Never trust anybody under 65", I was enjoying a delightful cocktail when something dawned on me. How do the airlines get away with charging $4 for a cocktail? Probably the same way they get away with charging $4 to watch one of their grainy "edited for airline use" movies. But that is not the point.

The point is that we seem to have a variety of unusual names for cocktails in this country. It seems that nobody orders a shot and a beer anymore, opting for a Mai Tai or a Seabreeze, and these exotic names seem to be grouped in different classifications.

You have the religious grouping of cocktails which include Christian Brothers Brandy, St. Pauli Girl, Benedictine, and a Bloody Mary without vodka known as the Virgin Mary. Now, I am not a legal expert by any means but I think that the real Virgin Mary has a legitimate right to sue somebody over the unauthorized use of her name.

And speaking of names, another category of cocktails are all named after people who may or may not be collecting royalties. These include the Shirley Temple (ginger ale and grenadine) the Shirley Temple Black (add India ink), Rob Roy, Tom Collins, Brandy Alexander, and Harvey Wallbanger. I think more people should have drinks named after them. A citizen like yourself should be able to walk into a tavern and order a Vince Foster, a Pee Wee Herman, or a Bob Packwood. Of course, I don't think I'd want to know what's in any of them.

The next drink category is the geographic category where cocktails are named for places. Here you would find the Blue Hawaii, Singapore Sling, California Cooler, Canadian Club, Long Island Iced Tea, the Manhattan, the Black Russian, Irish coffee, and, of course, Scotch. This makes one wonder why only certain geographic locales have been lucky enough to be honored with drink names. How come Manhattan and Long Island got drinks but not Brooklyn or the Bronx? They should have rough and tumble drinks that knock you on your butt and leave you without your wallet. You would think that New Orleans, long a hotbed of alcoholic consumption, would have its own drink, but all they can muster down there is a fruity concoction called the Hurricane. And speaking of fruity drinks, why hasn't anyone ever come up with a cocktail called the San Francisco Swish?

There is no drink called the Las Vegas even though it would be easy to make, just pour some watered down liquor in a fancy glass and serve it with a side of "chips".

I can think of a lot of geographic cocktails we could add to the list. What about one made out of brandy and Evian water that comes served with a feather? It's the French Tickler. Or what about a combination of sake and prune juice called the Orient Express. We could even have one from the Philippines that would be so strong it would make your legs buckle. It's name? The Manila Folder.

The next time you decide to imbibe in an adult beverage, I encourage you to consult your Rand-McNally Atlas and consider inventing a brand new cocktail that you could name for the locale of your choice. As for me, I'm going to sit down to a glass of lemon juice and vinegar...it's so bad it makes you sick....I call it the Chicago Cubs.

50

Wasted Away In Margarettaville, Or A Place Like It

If you have nothing to do during the first week in May, I highly suggest that you consider celebrating the holiday known as Cinco De Mayo. Cinco De Mayo is the Mexican equivalent of St. Patrick's Day meets Oktoberfest on their way to Mardi Gras..

Cinco De Mayo translates to "The Fifth Of Mayo" which is a pretty large bottle of Mayonnaise and the principle ingredient in the Cholesterol Margarita.

Actually, Cinco De Mayo means "The Fifth of May" and is a time for raucous celebration in Mexico. Mexicans like to use Cinco De Mayo as a reason to consume their body weight in tequila and stay awake through their siesta periods. Part of the party includes the popular piñata. A piñata is a figure of a person or animal that is beaten with large sticks until it renders candy and treats. A version of this game was practiced by the LAPD until a few years ago. They don't play it anymore because they got caught and two of them are currently playing the incarceration version of this game called "Hey pal, I think you dropped your soap." If you find yourself in Mexico on the Cinco of May, there are several things you should be aware of for a safe and sane celebration.

First, always be respectful of the culture of the country that you are visiting. Do not refer to every Mexican man you meet as "Pepe" or "Pedro". They all have different names just like we have. Refer to them as "Mister", or, in Spanish, "Señor". Use this form whenever addressing a Mexican man as in, "Señor, how is your lawn care business?" or "Here is my wallet Señor, please do not kill me."

By the same manner, Mexican women should not be referred to as "Mama Cita" but rather by "Señora" for a married woman or "Señorita" for a single woman. If you are not sure if a woman is married or single, use the Mexican version of Ms. which would be "Sa."

DO NOT DRINK TEQUILA ALONE! Tequila is a very strong drink and if consumed in excess will cause you to do strange things like agreeing to smuggle a family of 15 across the border in the trunk of your car. Only drink tequila with a trusted companion, preferably one who a) doesn't drink and b) has plenty of bail money. If you insist on drinking tequila alone, don't blame me if you wake up in the Ensenada countryside wearing only underpants and a Dodgers cap.

Remember that Mexicans speak a different language than we do. If you meet a Mexican who does not speak English you can NOT make him understand you simply by speaking louder and with an accent. Rely instead on the use of a standard English/Spanish travelers phrase book which includes translations for such crucial phrases as "I am a Protestant" and "I need an enema."

Above all, remember that no matter what anyone tells you, the celebration of Cinco De Mayo DOES NOT require that you attend a four hour time share sales presentation.

"Vaya Con Carne", or, as they say in Mexico, "Go With Meat.

51

Reading;
One Of The Things
That Makes Us Literate

I love to read and I assume you must love to read also, otherwise you wouldn't be holding this book in front of you now. This brings up an interesting philosophical point; if you buy a book and never read it does it make a sound?

Reading is fun for the whole family even though they might think that Nintendo or pay-per-view wrestling is more fun. Herein lies a major problem. How do we get our fellow Americans to read more? Well, I thought it would be a good idea if we could pass along some bibliographical suggestions to our non-reading friends in the hopes that it would encourage them to pick up a book. So, I went to my local book store and perused some interesting titles. Granted, I did not have the time to read each of these books, but I think the titles alone warrant a recommendation. Here's what I found. The titles are real, the descriptions I made up.

Be Your Own Dick *by John Q. Newman* - I'm not sure what this book is all about but it must have something to do with either detective work or some sort of Zen love making.

How To Read A Book *by Mortimer Adler and Charles Van Doren* - This is probably the first book you should get someone to read although it is really a Catch-22. How can they read a book about reading books if they can't read a book in the first place?

The MAFIA Cookbook *by Joseph "Joe Dogs" Ianuzzi* – "To make Stoolie Stew, you start with a dead stoolie, an onion, and lots of tomato sauce." What the heck kind of a book is this? Is it one of a series of great American cook books? What can we expect next, "Cooking With Friends" by Jeffrey Dahmer?

Jesus The Magician *by Motion Smith* - Is nothing sacred? It's bad enough that Penn & Teller show us how they do their tricks. I don't want to know how Jesus turned the water into wine or that he used a substitution trunk and a look-alike to raise Lazarus from the dead.

7 Centuries Of English Cooking *by M. de la Falaise* - Have you ever had English cooking? It is, without a doubt, the worst ersatz chow ever created. The English eat things like kidney pie, crumpets, and treacle. I can just imagine what 7 centuries of this garbage must taste like.

Old Polish Legends *by F. C. Anstruther* - Learn all about the man who could change a light bulb ALL BY HIMSELF and the inventor of the parachute that opens on impact.

52 I Wouldn't Get Buck Naked For A Hundred Bucks

By Eddie Lubitsch, The Last Angry Man

Nudity makes me sick. I don't like getting naked myself and I certainly don't like the thought of other people getting naked.

Don't misunderstand me, I can certainly see the ascetic appeal of a nubile Playboy centerfold, but we all know that those women do not really exist. They are the products of skillful computer imaging and the master strokes of an airbrush artist. Of the real people in the world today, few, if any, look good naked.

Think about it. Name me ten people that you would want to see in their birthday suits. Regis Philbin? Oprah? Dr. Ruth? Janet Reno? Boutros Boutros-Ghali? Don Knotts? Willard Scott? John Madden? The overwhelming answer is that there is not a single person alive today (and very few dead ones) that I would pay a nickel to see naked.

I am sure that some of you out there think old Eddie has finally flipped out. You think that I have become some sort of a senile, impotent bitter old fart who wouldn't recognize a nice pair of hooters if they slapped him in the face. Well, you are dead wrong my friend. I have nothing against hooters slapping me in the face. All that I am against is nudity because, for the most part, NAKED PEOPLE ARE UGLY.

Human bodies have numerous imperfections. Some sag in the wrong places. Some bulge in the wrong places. Some have multiple marks, scars and blemishes. And sometimes, there is just too much body for a single human being.

Now some of you are saying, "Hey, not every naked body is ugly, what about those dancers at Thee Nudie Bar?" Balderdash, I say. Those surgically altered, silicone injected, dipilitorized specimens are freaks of nature. They only appear to be attractive because of the special lighting.

Anyone who tells me that the naked human body is beautiful has obviously never been to a nude beach; otherwise known as Fellini's casting call. At a nude beach you see parts of the human fuselage which are normally covered up by a bathing suit. This is very distracting. When you try to hold a meaningful conversation with a naked person you soon find that you cannot look them in the eye. As you are talking, your glance is diverted towards the hanging flesh pods which dangle from almost everybody, and this will make you sick.

So, if you are a real American do us all a favor and keep your clothes on. Help to beautify America by wearing as many clothes as possible to cover up your repulsive nakedness. You may want to go so far as to turn off the bathroom lights when you take a shower so that you won't have to look at yourself naked. Nudity is not pretty in any form. If God would have wanted us to run around naked, he would have given us fur.

And it's extreme stretches of logic like this that make me the Last Angry Man.

That's all from me...for now.

53 Take Me Out To The Ball Game, If You Can Afford It

Baseball season is a time for fun, excitement, and total confusion. Lest you be confused by that last sentence, allow me to explain why baseball confuses more people than a joint session of Congress.

For years, baseball has been filled with confusing words and perplexing phrases that baseball fans see and hear but seldom comprehend. I make mention of this because one of these confusing terms is currently over 100 years old.

On June 16, 1894 the first *suicide squeeze play* was executed (no pun intended). For those of you unfamiliar with this term, the suicide squeeze play occurs when you have a runner on third base and less than two outs. The man in the batter's box, also known as the "batter" bunts the ball and runs to first. However, before he gets all the way to the bag, he grabs his throat and begins choking himself to death. Usually, the entire opposing team stops whatever they are doing and watches this player thrash around on the ground. While they are preoccupied, the runner on third slowly saunters to the plate and scores a run. Once he is safely home, the batter loosens his grip on his own throat and continues to first. Everybody is safe and the other team feels really stupid for falling for this old trick.

Now, if you didn't know about the suicide squeeze play, you may not know the real meanings of several other baseball terms. So, I am going to help set you straight with...

Dale's Guide To Baseball Terminology

Full Count. When a batter has two strikes and three balls...he finds it very difficult to walk. Ha, ha, ha. Gosh, I love a good ball joke. Seriously, when a player has two strikes and three balls, he automatically gets knighted by the Queen of England and becomes a Full Count. From there he can become a Viscount, a Discount, or even a Downforthe Count.

Double Play. A Double Play occurs during the first game of a Double Header when the batter hits a Double to a fielder with Double Vision, who, in turn, throws the ball on a Double Dare to the umpire/second baseman who is serving Double Duty. This places everyone in Double Jeopardy which, as we all know, has two Daily Doubles. This play was invented by the game's creator, Abner Doubleday.

Grand Slam. Two eggs, two pancakes, bacon and sausage. Available at your local Denny's.

Pepper. We have all seen the signs posted in the infields of major league ballparks that proclaim "No Pepper". These signs mean that someone on the home team is very allergic to this condiment and does not want any of it on the field of play. Some ballparks have different signs for different allergies. For instance, a sign in Seattle states "No Marjoram" and a sign in the ball park in Detroit reads "No Parsley, No Sage, No Rosemary, But Take Your Thyme".

Sacrifice. This is what every professional ball player makes to become a professional ball player. Instead of earning a living as a postal clerk or a dock worker, these brave men graciously accept bazillions of dollars to play a stupid kid's game.

Charging The Mound. A batter usually charges the pitcher's mound when he doesn't have enough to pay for it all in cash.

Balk. This term is a combination of two words, "Ball" and "Stalk" and refers to the practice of following a runner with the ball in your hand and without him knowing about it.

Around The Horn. This term refers to the first professional ball players who came to this country from Tierra del Fuego, thus having to travel "Around Cape Horn".

54

I'm Not Fat,
I'm Just Big Boned

The people of this country are getting fatter than ever and it is time to do something about it. Almost everyone in this country between the ages of 35 and 50 wants to lose weight because, quite frankly, almost everyone in this category is a porker. Oh sure, there are exceptions to this general overstatement but they are few and far between. Most of us from the President right on down to Oprah are carting around excess blubber and quite frankly, it is time to let it go.

Traditional dieting programs revolve around a combination of low fat/low calorie foods and strenuous regular exercise. Well no wonder they never work. Baby boomers do not have the will power to exercise on a regular basis nor do we have the anesthetized palates required for tofu and fiber cakes. We were born to sit on the sofa and eat Doritos all day. What we need is a weight loss program that is user friendly. Well, my friends, you have come to the right place, because I am pleased to announce...

Dale's Guaranteed Weight Loss Program

Step #1 on my weight loss program is to determine how much weight you want to lose. To calculate this figure, take a good look at yourself naked in a full length mirror. You will find that the amount of time you can look at yourself is inversely proportional to the total amount of weight you need to lose. For instance if you can stand to stare at your fat ass for only 5 or 6 seconds before you feel like digging your eyes out with a spoon, you need to lose about 50 pounds. But, if you can stare at your unclothed form for 30 minutes or more...you have a severe Narcissus complex and should seek professional help. If you fit between these two extremes, adjust your desired weight loss as needed.

Step #2 of the weight loss program is to get rid of all of the food currently in your home. If you have nothing to eat in the house you will wind up eating...nothing. It is a simple mathematical formula that works. To rid your home of food I recommend that you throw a major party and serve everything you have stored away in the cupboards, the refrigerator, and the freezer. Now I realize that food from the pantry could combine for a rather peculiar menu, but if you get your friends gooned up enough they might even ask for your recipe for Sara Lee Pound Cake with Mixed Vegetable Sauce or broken Graham Crackers On A Shingle. If you do not have any friends or are put off by serving a variegated menu like this, just get your dog stoned and he will eat everything you have...including the containers.

Step #3 involves extensive weight training and aerobic exercise. Since you now have nothing to eat in the house, you can feel free to exercise without having the worry of pigging out after your pushup. The exercise I highly recommend is weight lifting. The problem with weight lifting is that the weights used are often very heavy. Some have been known to weigh upwards of 10 pounds apiece. Weights of this size are very dangerous and could cause you to pull a muscle or pop a hernia. I suggest that you go with smaller weights of 12 ounces apiece. These weights can easily be purchased in the form of cans of beer. These handy exercise cylinders are available at many locations and can be purchased in convenient 6 packs for those wishing to increase their desired lifting weight (DLW) to 4.5 pounds. Carry these weights with you wherever you go so that during moments of downtime and/or traffic lights, you can pick them up and pump some aluminum. After you are through lifting for the day do not discard your weights as they can be used for step #4.

Step #4 is the final step and revolves around eating sensibly. Eventually you will have to consume some kind of nourishment or else you will die. Don't get me wrong, you will look nice and thin when you die but you will die. Most experts suggest that a low fat regimen is the only way to go for weight loss and I couldn't agree more. If you are what you eat, as my grandmother used to say, then it only makes sense that fat people eat fat while skinny people eat no fat. After exhaustive research, I have developed a list of foods which contain absolutely no fat. They are as follows:

BEER

How convenient that you already have plenty of beer weights lying around. Whenever you feel hungry, pop the top on one of your weights and enjoy a nice refreshing NON FAT beverage. If you find yourself becoming light headed after one beer you are what is called a "cheap date". If this is the case, have two more beers immediately and go to bed. You will wake up refreshed in the morning and ready for another intensive day of weight loss. Follow this procedure until you lose all the weight you desire or until you are admitted to the Betty Ford Clinic, whichever comes first.

55

Hey You Kids,
Get Offa My Lawn

For some reason, lawns are a big deal in the suburbs of midwestern cities. As a child growing up on a city sized lot, I learned the importance of lawn care. In the glory years of the 50's and 60's a person's lawn represented a traditional American value and was to be prized. Your lawn ranked right up there in importance with robust tomato plants and a paneled basement. As the youngest member of my family, my right of passage included a stint as the family groundskeeper.

This all important responsibility is traditionally passed on to the youngest male by the father who not only values his lawn but looks upon it as his contribution to "the fruited plain." In my family, the importance of a good looking lawn was passed on by my mother. My dad had absolutely no interest in the lawn, figuring that if it all turned brown it would be his contribution to the "amber waves of grain." He thought that as long as the lawn was green, you shouldn't mess with it. To him, it did not make a big difference if that green color emanated from grass, weeds, or penicillin laden mold spores. Green was green.

My mother, on the other hand, really knew her fescue from her zoysia. She wanted her lawn to be mowed, trimmed, edged, fertilized, aerated, and dethatched on a regular basis...usually every Saturday morning. After the cutting, the weeds had to be pulled and new seed added. All in all, the lawn maintenance job was a pain in the butt.

My first real job while still living at home was in a cemetery where I spent 90% of my time CUTTING

THE GRASS. Needless to say, I really hated cutting grass.

Now I am a responsible adult with grass of my own...far too much grass of my own. I have no idea what I was thinking when the real estate agent sold me a house on "a nice sized yard." I must have thought that the house came with its own 12 year old boy for lawn care. Well, it didn't. Once again I was spending my life cutting grass.

I bought a power mower along with a spreader, a gas trimmer, and a device which produces a very strong blast of air so that you can send grass clippings into your neighbor's yard. It is especially fun to pull this blower out at Christmas time and play Hurricane Hugo with the toy village under the tree. I used all of these outdoor appliances a total of three or four times before a team of illegal immigrants pulled in my driveway and offered to relieve me of my summertime drudgery.

The point of the matter is that I have had decades of lawn care experience. I also have more seldom used lawn care equipment than a mentally balanced individual should own. Therefore, I look upon myself as somewhat of a lawn expert. You can call me Lawn Boy, and here are my five favorite lawn care tips.

Five Favorite Lawn Care Tips

1. To keep neighborhood dogs from making unauthorized deposits on your lawn, scatter several mousetraps baited with a dollop of Ken-L-Ration. Not only will the dogs stop dumping on your parkway, they'll cross the street to avoid it.

2. Water your lawn with a mixture of water and latex paint...preferably green, although if you really want

to be the envy of the neighbors, go for a nice blue tinge.

3. Livestock make excellent organic grass trimmers. Check your local ordinances for keeping goats, cows, or sheep.

4. Burrowing animals are bad for your lawn. Creatures like moles, gophers, or U.S. Senators should be eliminated by trapping or term limits.

5. One word, Astroturf.

How To Become Rich And Famous

56

People often come up to me on the street and say, "Hey pal, your fly is open." Well, that's embarrassing enough, but the point is that no one ever comes up to me and says, "Hey, aren't you that famous funny author fella? And, you know your fly is open?"

Let's face it, if you want to be recognized in this country, you have to be either rich or famous. Everyone else is forced to amble through life in virtual anonymity. I have often wondered what it would be like to be rich and famous. How would it feel to get the good seats in the best restaurants? Heck, how would it feel to just GET INTO the best restaurants? I have wondered what it would be like to have people pester me for autographs or to have women throw their room keys to me on stage. Then, one day, it dawned on me that there must be a way to get rich or famous without having to work real hard.

Since I am currently neither rich nor famous, you may not think that I am qualified to write about this subject. But I would say to you that there are thousands of people who give advice on subjects they know nothing about. They are known as consultants.

So in my capacity as consultant, I have prepared a list of things you should do to become wealthy and well known. If any of them work for you please let me know and I might try them also.

Part I
How To Become Rich

1. **Be born to rich parents**. Ninety per cent of the rich people out there today were born to rich parents. This is called "being born with a silver spoon in your mouth." I was born with a plastic spork in my mouth. If I had it to do over again my parents would definitely be rich.

2. **Win the lottery**. If you can't be born rich, win your fortune in the lotto. There are hundreds of uneducated goobers out there who just happened to hit big in the lottery and are now set for life. These are the people that you should grab as your new set of parents. After you get them to adopt you, you can rob them blind because, admit it, they're not that smart because they won $50 million and still have their day job down at the varnish plant.

3. **Invent something**. If you can't win money or inherit money, all you have to do is invent something for which the gullible public will give you money. You don't have to invent anything that will alter the path of history, in fact, the dumber your invention, the more money you'll probably make. Take a look at the millions of dollars made by the likes of the Pet Rock, the Chia Pet, the Garden Weasel, or aerosol Hair-In-A-Can.

4. **Steal**. If you can't get rich any other way, you'll have to take it. There are many different ways to steal including burglary, robbery, televangelism, or getting elected to Congress. If you are a really good thief/congressperson, you may also become famous like Michael Milkin, Dan Rostenkowski, or Oral Roberts.

Part II
How To Become Famous

Since fame and wealth do not always go hand in hand, there are some things you can do to become independently famous. If you are famous, you may not get rich right away, but after you have been on Oprah, 20-20, Geraldo, and Jerry, people will probably be stuffing dollars in your face.

1. **Gain name recognition.** The first step to fame is to have people recognize your name. This can be established at the entry level by having yourself paged constantly. Have yourself paged at airports, bus terminals, restaurants, and Las Vegas casinos. If you do this on an average of 400 times each day, you will soon find yourself gaining celebrity status.

2. **Have a drink named after yourself.** This is a variation on the theme of inventing something covered in PART I. But, since it is virtually impossible to collect a royalty from every drink named after you, you'll just have to settle for the notoriety. Look what drinks have done for otherwise unknown people like Harvey Wallbanger, Tom Collins, or Bud Weiser.

3. **Change your name.** If you just can't wait for recognition of your own name, change it to something that already has fame attached. Don't pick an obvious name like Michael Jordan or Bob Hope, but go for something more subtle that people will have heard before but just won't remember where. Good choices include Geoffrey Chaucer, Francõis Truffaut, or Samuel Gompers.

4. **Get your face on a stamp.** Have you ever noticed

that people who appear on U.S. postage stamps are usually famous. Unfortunately they are also usually dead. Since you are probably still alive, you will have to settle for printing your own stamps. All you have to do is find a qualified printer and have them make up 32 cent stamps with your likeness. Then, put them on any envelope you can get your hands on. Chances are the post office won't notice anything wrong since they print up 50 or 60 different stamps every month and can't be expected to recognize all of them. Plus, if you get caught you will wind up on the front page of USA Today.

5. **Television, television, television.** Without a doubt, television is the surest way to make yourself famous. Look what TV did for that rainbow-wigged zealot who shows up on all of the football games. The same can happen for you. Start off by standing behind reporters as they broadcast from a fire or a political rally. Then, when you are sure the camera is on, jump up and down behind them and wave your arms over your head wildly. From there you can move up to higher exposure like being in the audience of The Jerry Lewis Telethon or being featured on America's Most Wanted.

Follow these simple steps and you should be rich and famous in no time. Then again, this may all just be a crock.

The Theory Of Vegetablism

57

In today's health conscious society we are very aware of what we eat. In fact, the old adage of "you are what you eat" is popping up more and more in polite conversation. Well, if this is true, I'm a vegetable.

I consider myself a vegetarian because I eat primarily vegetables. I am not, however, a militant vegetarian. In addition to vegetables I eat fish because fish are stupid creatures that deserve to be eaten. And I eat chicken because it tastes just like frog legs. But I don't eat anything from which I could possibly be a descendant. I guess that means I am not really a vegetarian but more of a Darwinian who prefers not to eat his own kind.

Real vegetarians believe in eating only things that come from the ground like plants, fruits, and asphalt. They make their steaks out of tofu, their burgers out of lentils, and their Thanksgiving turkeys out of seaweed and a Jell-O mold. They do this because they are followers of a belief known as Vegetablism. Vegetablism is a secret society not unlike the Masons or the Rosicrucians except they have no special handshakes and do not advertise in the National Enquirer.

Recently I was able to go under cover and crack the deepest secrets of the Vegetablists. As a serious journalist and under penalty of Death by Eggplant, I bring you the heretofore unknown secrets of the Vegetablists.

Vegetablists base their beliefs on the ancient Vegetable Scrolls discovered in a cave near Santa Fe, New

Mexico in the late 1940's. This secret manuscript was written by the first Vegetablists, a peaceful tribe from Iowa. Since this tribe never traveled further than their local health food store, we can only wonder how the scrolls wound up in New Mexico.

The secrets of Vegetablism revolve around the basic concept that vegetables rule the world and that humans exist only to make them grow. They believe that all of the vegetables in the world have an effect on all other living things and, depending on when you were born, will have an effect on you too.

True Vegetablists follow their Vegescopes in the daily paper and believe that the vegetable sign under which a person is born will determine their personality. Here are a few of the Vegescope traits I was able to jot down before I was caught and forced to eat carrots until my skin turned yellow.

The Creamed Corn (January 15 - February 14) People born under the sign of Creamed Corn are nutty people who will do anything for a laugh. This is because creamed corn, as we all know, is the funniest of all the vegetables. If you do not believe me, just open a can of creamed corn and pour it over your head. You will get laughs for hours - something which just doesn't happen with lima beans or hearts of palm.

Famous corn signs include Jerry Lewis, Soupy Sales, and Gerald Ford.

Brussels Sprouts (March 3 - April 1) Those lucky enough to be born under the sign of the sprouts are truly blessed. Sprouts are happy people who love to be around other happy people. Sprouts born with Parsley on the cusp and Butter on the side are the happiest of all. Sprout people are not the smartest folks you will ever meet, but they have a love of life that allows you to overlook their simple-mindedness and take advantage of their gullibility. If you think you need a horse to play water polo, you are most likely a Sprout.

Famous Sprouts include people who send in their Publisher's Clearing House Sweepstakes entry forms and anyone who voted for Marion Barry.

Kohlrabi (May 10-12) Kohlrabi is a mysterious sign. no one ever knows what you are. Are you a Radish (April 25 - May 9) or are you a Cabbage (May 13 - June 1)? No one ever knows for sure because you taste like a combination of both.

The person born under Kohlrabi is a true enigma. You never know where they are, where they are headed, or how they achieved the level of success they currently enjoy. In other words, Kohlrabis lead you to wonder how they ever got to where they are today. They are puzzling. They are curious. They have no discernible skills.

Famous Kohlrabis include Zsa Zsa Gabor, Tom Arnold, and that guy who does the Amazing Discoveries infomercials.

Beets (February 29) The sign of the Beet is a nasty sign and people born under it have very few friends...if they have any at all. It is a good thing that Beet signs are only born once every four years. Beet signs are disliked because beets themselves are disliked. Think about it, do you know of anyone who actually likes beets? The only people who eat beets are Russians and I think that pretty much says it all.

Drunken beet signs are the worst of all. They are called pickled beets. Beet signs usually have ruddy complexions and sour dispositions. It is best to avoid them whenever possible lest they turn to physical violence and want to beet you up. If this happens, you will have to call a cop on the beet and hope that the beet who beet you doesn't beet the rap.

Famous Beet signs include Saadam Hussein, Jeffrey Dahmer, and Art Modell.

Swiss Chard (November 23 - December 15) The sign of Swiss Chard is the most neutral of all the signs. Swiss Chards are just the opposite of Beets, never wanting to pick a fight or provoke an argument. Chards are also very industrious workers, in fact, you could set your Swiss watch by a Chard. Swiss Chards can also be multi-faceted. One side of them is sharp as a knife, while another side of them is as dull as a can opener. This trait is usually found in an offshoot of the Chard family called the Swiss Army Chard.

Famous Swiss Chards include Albert Einstein, Clark Kent, and most street mimes.

58

Pc Or Not Pc,
That Is The Question

So much is being made nowadays about being Politically Correct that it is enough to make you puke. Unfortunately, PUKE is not a politically correct term. Instead I should say that it is enough to cause you serious gastro-intestinal distress with a possibility of regurgitation.

That is one of the problems with America today. We have become too sensitive for our own good. I think we have all experienced the phenomenon of being corrected for saying MAILMAN instead of the more politically correct LETTER CARRIER. And, by now we must all realize that the person who brings you bad food on an airplane is not a STEWARDESS, but rather a FLIGHT ATTENDANT.

Access holes to the city sewer system are no longer known as MANHOLES but must now be called PERSONHOLES, capped off with PERSONHOLE COVERS. An alternative name for manholes is $\Delta\beta\approx\Omega$ – "The hole formerly known as manhole."

I guess what I am trying to say is that it is time to stop trying to please everybody. Rather than trying to be politically correct, let's just settle for common sense...if it still exists. Imagine what our classic literature would be like if the authors had been so concerned with political correctness that they lost sight of their story. As an example, I have recreated three of our all time favorite nursery rhymes using politically correct terminology. You be the judge.

PC Old Mother Hubbard

Senior citizen Ms. Hubbard,

Went to the cupboard, *(Not because she HAD to because it was stereotypical of her gender, but rather because she WANTED to for her own reasons and for her desire to grow as a person.)*

To get her underprivileged Canine-American a bone. *(Not a REAL bone, mind you, which would require the raising of a methane-producing, ozone-destroying, Bovine-American, but rather a processed bone made from whole wheat, barley, oat bran, and bulgur, pressed into a bone shape.)*

But when she got there,

The cupboard was bare, *(Principally because she was a senior citizen on a fixed income and the government was late AGAIN with her monthly check, thus forcing her to eat the dog food normally reserved for the aforementioned Canine-American.)*

And so her economically deprived Canine-American had none.

PC Little Jack Horner

Stature impaired Jack Horner

Sat in a corner

Eating his Christmas/Hanukkah/Holiday pie.

He stuck in his thumb,

And was photographed by Robert Maplethorp who said, "That's good, now try putting your thumb in the PIE."

PC Little Miss Muffet

Junior citizen Ms. Muffet,

Sat on a tuffet,

Eating her high fiber, low fat, curds and whey.

Along came a spider,

And sat down beside her,

And Ms. Muffet, utilizing her Ph.D. in Animal Biology, immediately recognized the arachnid as a Peruvian Spotted Spider and an endangered species.

So she lobbied Congress to ban tuffet sitting in that portion of the country even though it would cost the jobs of thousands of professional tuffet sitters who could, nonetheless, be retrained for other professions.

59

Give A Man A Fish,
And He'll Eat For Today.
Teach A Man To Fish
And He'll Spend A Lot Of Money On Tackle

Fishing is one of the great universal pastimes, ranking right up there with baseball and following the endless saga of OJ Simpson. I remember when my dad used to take me fishing. I was just a boy but he would take me to the shores of Lake Erie and teach me how to fish for perch. My tackle consisted of a rod, reel, hook, sinker, and bobber. We would fish for a few hours, maybe an afternoon. We would talk, and laugh, and eat the sandwiches that my mom packed for us in the Coleman cooler. If we caught fish it would be great. If we didn't, well, I guess we'd have hamburgers for dinner.

These are my memories of fishing...a peaceful, fun, relaxing experience. It was something that in my hectic stress-ridden life I had almost forgotten. It is no wonder that when my friend Kevin invited me to join him on a fishing "expedition" I jumped at the chance, remembering my relaxing times on the shores of Lake Erie. But as we neared the expedition date, I began to recognize some significant changes from the fishing I remembered.

First of all, we were not going to one of the Great Lakes for our adventure but rather to a foreign sounding place called Minaki in the upper regions of Canada. And we were not going fishing for a few hours but for FIVE DAYS! Still, it sounded like fun. I figured we would fish for an hour or two and then hit the pool, have some beers, and hit the night life. Enter, the VACATION FROM HELL.

For starters, Minaki is over 1000 miles from Chicago, requiring two days of sitting in a car with three other people and trying not to get car sick. Ever since childhood I have been cursed with auto-motion-intestinal-disorder. It was agreed that I would let my fishing partners drive to Minaki while I flew since I am a seasoned air traveler. I should say that I am a seasoned air traveler on big commercial jets. My trip to Minaki was on a twelve seat antique that still had Orville Wright's autograph on the wing. Between Chicago and Minaki this plane made 6 stops; three for gas, two for passengers, and one to ask directions. It was certainly an adventure in aviation.

I met my fellow anglers at the Minaki airport...rather the "Minaki Strip Of Blacktop In The Middle Of The Woods", and we made our way to the lodge that was to be our home for the next five days. Driving through Minaki reminded me of Mayberry. It was small, quiet, and on the way we passed signs that let us know we were in Canada. Signs like, "Leeches By The Pound" and "Beer By The Tanker Truck". Now I was getting very excited. I had never seen a pound of leeches before.

Before I could even get nauseous, we were at the Birch Island Lodge, a beautifully quaint fishing lodge ON AN ISLAND. In fact, the Birch Island Lodge was the only thing on the island...because there was no room to put anything else. I was stuck on an island smaller than a K Mart parking lot FOR FIVE DAYS. We had no TV, no newspapers, and the only radio station we could get broadcast in French. Also, the pool I envisioned was absent as was the night life. This place catered to the extremely serious fisherman. Only 24 fisherpeople could be housed at the lodge on any given day. We all ate together, listened to French radio together, and at night, sat around and did nothing together.

Breakfast was served every morning at 7AM, a

time normally reserved for REM sleep. But up here, I was wide awake, primarily because my room was right next to the kitchen, and the kitchen help took great pleasure in fixing breakfast as noisily as possible. I swear they were forcibly extracting the eggs from the chickens and thrashing their own wheat to make flour for the bread. After breakfast it was off to the boats for a day filled with the sounds of the loon and the smell of bait.

At first, fishing was everything I remembered it to be. There was the fresh air, the camaraderie, and, of course, the fish. There were very many fish. I caught my limit by 10:30AM and thought we would be back at the lodge by noon. Instead, we stopped for lunch, ate the fish we had just caught, and headed out to catch more fish. All told, we spent 8 hours sitting on our asses in the boat. But this was just day 1. By the end of our stay, I estimate that I spent 50 hours sitting, 12 hours untangling my line, and 6 hours proclaiming, "That little bastard ate my bait."

Day #2 of my adventure started out pretty much like day #1 except the kitchen help decided to come to work early...It was French Toast Day. We fished for what seemed like an eternity before we got caught in the HAIL STORM! Out of nowhere, a hail storm from Armageddon hit us like a Lilliputian mortar attack. Chunks of ice the size of your proverbial golf ball were pelting us and exploding on contact. Now I know what Jupiter must feel like.

The remaining days in Minaki are all one big blur to me now. Wake up, go fishing, eat fish, go fishing some more, have dinner (fish), and sit around and talk about fish with the other 23 men in the lodge. It was becoming obvious to me that fishing was a sport with a very narrow focus. These people were serious about their fishing. Quite honestly, I thought they were all nuts until it happened to me....THE DAY OF THE LUNKER.

On our last day, we were fishing for walleye and bass, and anything else that would bite on a hook when they started telling me about THE LUNKER. Apparently, there were some really big fish in these waters that the locals referred to as "lunkers". I found out later that "lunker" is an old Indian word for "really big fish". Lunkers can reach several feet in length and can weigh as much as a small child. I was told that they only went for certain kinds of bait tied to certain types of line, attached to certain types of rods.

Well, as the old pros were telling me riveting lunker yarns, I put down my rod to open up my first beer of the day. When I did that, something happened to my rod. It bent in half. I quickly grabbed it (after finding a safe place for my beer) and started to reel in whatever was on the other end of the line. "Lunker!" one of the men shouted. "Lunker my ass" I shouted back, "This is a really big fish."

I played this fish like Pavorotti plays the cello. I just pulled and reeled until I thought I felt an aneurysm coming on. About that time I saw The Lunker! It approached the boat like a piscine attack sub, not sure whether to continue this game of Tug of War, or charge into the side of the boat and sink it. This wasn't a fish, it was Moby Dick himself. After several hours (or so it seemed) I worked the fish to the side of our boat. "Get a net under it" one of the old pros shouted. "I don't have Annette with me...or any of the other Mouseketeers for that matter" I shouted back. With that, the lunker gave a mighty tug on the line, and with all of his strength snapped it in two.

I watched as the lunker disappeared into the water with my hook in his mouth, and wondered how he was going to explain it to his wife. He got away but it was all right. Normally all they do with lunkers is shellac them and hang them on an office wall. I still had the warm glow of accomplishment after finally understanding what drew people to this sport. It was the hunt, the capture, the struggle between man and beast. I felt so alive with this knowledge that I stood up in the boat and shouted, "Today I am a fisher-man."

"You let him get away, today you are a putz" shouted the old pros.

60

Everything I Have Is Short

An editorial by Eddie Lubitsch, The Last Angry Man

I have never been a fan of big things. In fact, most big things make me uneasy. I don't like the Sears Tower in Chicago because it is the tallest building in the world. Do you realize what would happen if it were to ever fall over? It would really snarl traffic. I also don't like those exceptionally tall professional basketball players. You know the ones. Players like Manute Bol and Shawn Bradley who are over 9 feet tall and can dunk with their elbows. There is no reason for a person to be this tall. Just imagine if they ever fall over on a busy street. There goes traffic again. And I don't like big long lines like you would find at Disney World. These are the lines for the special exhibits like Mickey's Synapse Scrambler, or the Epcot feature "Inside Michael Jackson's Glove." The only reason anyone would have to stand in a line this long would be to obtain food for a starving family or to catch a glimpse of the cast of "Baywatch" naked.

The point of the matter is that I hate things that are bigger, longer, and taller than they really need to be. I normally prefer things that are short. This is because, by today's standards I would be considered a short man. I can live with this. I can also live with the fact that I am shortsighted, have a short attention span, enjoy wearing shirts with short sleeves, used to play shortstop, listen to short-wave radio, and my favorite meal consists of short ribs, short bread, and a short beer all served up by a short order cook who usually tries to short change me. Short is not so bad except when it comes to the month of February.

As you are aware, February is the shortest month

of the year since it contains only 28 days. Once every four years though, the people who make the calendars feel sorry for February and award it an extra day thus temporarily giving it 29 days. After this happens, February must slink back to it's 28 day capacity for three more years.

This may not sound like a big deal to you but how would you have liked to be born on February 29th? This is what happened to me and it still gets under my skin like a tick in a rainstorm. I only get to celebrate my birthday once every four years and this stinks.

Even when I was a little Lubitsch, my parents relished in the fact that they did not have to shell out for presents and a cake except in years when they voted for president. The rest of the time they would tease me unmercifully by telling me on February 28th, "Well Eddie, tomorrow is your birthday." Then, on the next day they would tell me, "Today's not your birthday, today is March 1st." For years I was convinced that I had slept through my birthday. This sucks bigger than a lamprey in love.

It is time for me and thousands like me to stand up for our natal day rights and fight the system. I want February 29th added back into our calendars EVERY YEAR. I am sick and tired of the 29th being a part time day and think it should have equality with the other 365 days in the year. This country was based on the premise that all men are created equal but it says nothing about all <u>days</u> being equal. It is time to fight back.

Not only do I want February 29th to be put on a par with other days but I want it declared a national holiday to make up for the years of abuse it has taken. In fact, I may just sue to have this idea implemented retroactively. I want every day to be February 29th for a full year to compensate for my years of chronological abuse. I want Christmas to fall on February 29th, as well as Thanksgiving, Labor Day, and Mother's Day. I even want the 4th of July moved to the 29th of February. Dammit, they owe me this much.

If you were born on February 29th or are at least sympathetic to my cause, I want you to make your voice known. Write your congresspeople and tell them to cancel the debate on welfare reform and health care until they straighten out this February debacle. If that doesn't work we will take to the streets and make our feelings known. We may even have to break into a few calendar supply shops and throw paint on their calendars until they see that we are right. We can march on Washington DC while chanting something original like "2,4,6,8, fix the damn calendars or we're really going to get mad." I know it doesn't rhyme but I think it makes our point.

We may be told that there isn't enough time to make a full time February 29th without increasing the growing national menology deficit but I say this is a crock of bullspit. They could take a day from one of the greedy months like January or March to bring February closer to equality. Or, we could just add another day to the year. Who's going to know? Maybe in two or three hundred years when the calendar no longer jibes with the earth's rotation and winter falls in July somebody may get suspicious but we'll all be dead so what the heck. We have to do something and we have to do it now.

So rise up America and demand the permanent return of February 29th.. And when you get it, it would sure be nice if you called it "Eddie Lubitsch ⌐

And it's delusional thinking like me The Last Angry Man.

That's all from me...for now.

61

An Editorial

By Eddie Lubitsch,
The Last Angry Man

"March Comes In Like A Lion And Goes Out Like A Lamb." This clever phrase was given to us by the ancient Greek philosopher Homer in about 900 BC. At least this is the translation we have today. What Homer really said was "March Comes In Like One Of Those Animals That Eats Christians And Goes out Like One Of Those Animals We Like To Chase Around The Barn Yard Late At Night When We Are Very Lonely." But no matter how you slice it, it means the same thing, HOMER WAS A STRANGE MAN.

That not withstanding, let me get on to the real issue of the day. March means the start of spring training and spring training means the start of baseball. Now I am as red blooded as the next guy, and even more so if the next guy happens to be Mr. Spock. I like motherhood and apple pie, but I am having a major problem with baseball.

Baseball has ceased to be America's favorite pastime. America's favorite pastime has become flipping through the TV channels with the remote control, or calling one of those 1-900 numbers. Baseball has slipped to a dismal third. And why? Because baseball has ceased being a sport and has become a business. Everywhere you turn you read about contract negotiations, ticket prices, performance incentives and million dollar deals. What in the name of Nap Lajouie is going on here?

The ultimate insult came from Seattle, (Home Of The Never Empty Cistern) where the owner of the Seahawks thought about selling the team to THE JAPANESE! Well slice my wrists and hang me out to dry. Could you even imagine a major league baseball team being owned by foreigners?

First, they'd probably change the name to the Seattle Sushi. Then they'd make the fans go through 20 minutes of calisthenics before they start the game. And we would probably all have to leave our shoes at the front gate. The possibilities are endless.

Then, the Germans would probably buy a team and change the uniforms to lederhosen and Tyrolean caps. Relief pitchers would be brought out of the dugout in BMWs. And we would all have to clean up after ourselves before we could leave the stadium.

Next, the French will buy a team and there goes the chance to buy a good hot dog at the game. They would change all of the concessions to that wimpy frog food like crepes and fois gras. Then, they would name Jerry Lewis as the general manager. On the plus side, topless sun bathing would be encouraged in the bleachers.

I think you can see where I am headed with this and it is not pretty sight. We have to stop foreign ownership of American baseball before it is too late or before you know it our teams will have names like The French Ticklers, The Brussels Sprouts, or The Spanish Fly.

And it's futuristic worries like this that make me....the last angry man.

That's all from me....for now.

62

Our Friend The Beer

I like beer. I like beer a lot. In fact, I like a lot of beer. Therefore, May 6th is the perfect day for a guy like me because it is National Home Brew Day. This is the day to celebrate those who attempt to brew their own beer at home. I respect people who can do this because it is good to have a hobby that can give you a buzz. It is also good to have a hobby that helps you create the most perfect of all of nature's beverages.

Beer is indeed the most perfect beverage of all, and I have the statistics to back it up. Well, maybe they're not statistics, but they are pretty good arguments. I have listed them below under the heading...

Why beer is nature's most perfect beverage..

1. It was meant to be consumed in quantity. Unlike other beverages, beer is seldom sold one can at a time. There are no beer vending machines. It is sold by the six pack, the 12 pack, or the 24 piece case. AND, if you do happen to be able to buy a single bottle of beer, it is generally a quart bottle.

2. Beer has it's own physical trait named after itself. Granted, other beverages have physical traits also like the milk mustache, or coffee breath, but only beer has been given the unique distinction which separates its consumers from the rest...the beer belly. This should not be confused with the beer bust which is not a distinction of large machungas on female beer drinkers, but rather the act of getting arrested for carrying an open beer in your car. If you are arrested on a beer bust and you do not have any beer in your possession, you have been illegally detained and are a victim of what is known as the beer frame.

3. Beer makes ugly people look better. I know they only look better for a short time, but if it wasn't for beer, many people would look butt-ugly all of the time.

4. Beer exercises the kidneys. Your kidneys need a workout just like the rest of your body, but the only way to accomplish this is from the inside. Gallons of beer cursing through your kidneys on their way to the bladder is the perfect way to make sure that this internal organ gets a full aerobic workout. As an added benefit, the use of beer will also exercise legs since you will be walking to the bathroom every ten minutes.

5. Drink eight glasses of water a day! This is the advice the health professionals have been giving us for decades. Well, let me ask you this, what is the prime ingredient in beer? It's water, of course. Beer is over 95% water. And the other five percent are nutritious things like barley, hops, and yeast...tasty ingredients also found in bread. So, instead of drinking eight glasses of water a day and eating bread, have yourself a dozen beers.

6. Not only is beer a refreshing beverage, but it doubles as a shampoo. Millions of women wash their hair with beer to restore luster and bounce to their locks. Men only use beer on their heads in locker room celebrations.

7. Beer is the official drink of St. Patrick's Day. What other beverage has been connected with a major holiday as strongly as beer is with St. Patty's Day? The correct answer is NONE. People may think about champagne on New Year's Eve or wine on

Bastille Day, but only St. Patrick's Day serves up GREEN beer as the beverage du jour.

8. If it weren't for beer, there'd be no football. Think about it, America's beer makers sponsor 90% of our professional football games. In fact, beer is the only beverage to have its own bowl game. You won't see the Bottled Water Bowl or the Cranberry Juice Bowl or even the Decaffeinated Coffee Bowl, but every American is very familiar with the Bud Bowl. 'Nuff said.

9. Everything about beer is recyclable. You can re-cycle the cans to make airplane wings. You can recycle the bottles to make new bottles. You can even recycle the kegs to make a pretty snappy barbecue grill. But the real beauty of beer is that it recycles within the human system. After all, we all know that you can't buy beer, you can only rent it.

10. You do not need any special equipment to enjoy beer. Every other beverage requires some sort of ancillary apparatus to achieve total enjoyment. Champagne requires a champagne glass; wine calls for a wine glass; milk demands cookies for total enjoyment; and even water is now served with a slice of lemon. But beer alone needs nothing to stand between it and its consumer. Beer can be poured in a glass, but it is most frequently en-joyed right out of the bottle or can. Beer doesn't even necessitate refrigeration, as it is served warm in some parts of the world.

11. Beer can be consumed anywhere. You can enjoy a beer in a beer joint, a beer garden, or a beer hall. Beer can be enjoyed at home, or on the ride home. Beer is served at sporting events, the ballet, and more enjoyable wakes. It is equally at home with

peanuts or pate and is truly a beverage for the people. So stand up America and enjoy your beer. And while you're up, get me a cold one from the fridge.

63

This Is The Last Page

Congratulations, you have made it to the end of the book.

If this were a mystery novel, this page would have contained the final solution of "whodunit."

If this were a dictionary, this page would have contained the words "zoot suit" and "zwieback."

If this were a text book, the last page would contain the answers.

Alas, this is only a humor book and under the code established by the International Association of Humor Book Writers, the only thing required on this page is the following cryptic statement.....

Buy more of these books as gifts. Buy anything you can find by this author. Live long and prosper.

The End